MarketPlace	: AUK
Order Number	: 205-5051982-4369928
Ship Method	: Standard
Order Date	: 2014-10-28
Email	: dvnv4718w79b3r0@marketplace.amazon.co.uk

Items : 1

Qty	Item	Locator
1	Dr. Clock\'s Handbook	MUL-2-BF-03-075-9
	ISBN : 187000339X	RY

RCode:

~erry House, Woods Way, Goring By Sea, West Sussex, BN12 4QY. Tel:+44(0)1903 507544
: sales@worldofbooks.com | Twitter: @WorldofBooksltd | Web: www.worldofbooks.com

Dr. Clock's Handbook

Let's absurdify life,

from East to West.

FERNANDO PESSOA

Arman's *Column of Clock Faces* outside Gare St.Lazare, Paris. Photograph by Michael Woods

Dr.Clock's

H A N D B O O K

EDITED BY MEL GOODING AND JULIAN ROTHENSTEIN

REDSTONE PRESS, LONDON

First published in 2006 by
Redstone Press, 7a St Lawrence Terrace, London W10 5SU
www.redstonepress.co.uk

ISBN 10: 1 870003 39 X
ISBN 13: 978 1 870003 39 1

Design: Julian Rothenstein
Artwork: Terence Smiyan
Production: Tim Chester
Printed and bound in China by C & C Offset Printing Co., Ltd

British Library Cataloguing-in-Publication Data
A catalogue record for this book is available from the British Library

Grateful acknowledgement is made to the following consultants:

Peter Blegvad, Adam Dant, Glen Baxter, Rhiannon Gooding, Natalie Howe, Daisy Cockburn

Many thanks also to: Alastair Brotchie, John Kador, Richard Prince, Ed Ruscha,
Nina Katchadourian, Wim Delvoye, Simon Patterson, Julie Lawson, Rosemary Kasmir, Hiang Kee,
Anne Clarke, Serpent's Tail, Penguin Books.

We acknowledge the first appearance of Dr. Clock in Ruth Fainlight's story
Dr. Clock's Last Case, from the volume of the same name published by Virago in 1994

Cover: based on an image by Joan Brossa

C O N T E N T S

1751

That year Diderot began to publish his Encyclopaedia, and the first
insane asylum was founded in London.

So the counting out began, to separate the sane, who veil themselves in
words, from the insane, who rip off feathers from their bodies.

Poets had to learn tightrope-walking.

And to make sure, officious types began to publish instructions on how
to be normal.

                                    MIROSLAV HOLUB

PREFACE

'The more precisely the position is determined, the less precisely the momentum is known in this instant, and vice versa.' (Werner Heisenberg on the uncertainty principle, 1927)

Seeing, as they say, is believing. But the world is not always as we see it to be. The Cubists, friends of physicists, demonstrated with elegance that the world is not only what we see, but also what we know to be the case. If, however, our knowledge is defective, as it must be, then the world may not be either as we see it *or* as we know it. What is more, our mind makes sense of things depicted that are impossible in the everyday world but perfectly logical within the world as pictured: consider Escher's endless staircase, or Alice's croquet lawn, or any surrealist painting by Magritte. On the other hand, there are times when we find it hard to believe in what we know to be true: for example, that the Möbius strip we have made by twisting and looping a rectangle of paper has indeed only *one* edge and *one* side.

Uncommonsense often makes a lot of sense. It might in the end make bearable the unbearable absurdity of being. When the knight errant of La Mancha rides forth he believes, against all the evidence of Sancho Panza's eyes, that what he sees is indeed what is the case, and by his conviction achieves a truly gallant dignity. When Dr. Pangloss observes complacently that were it not for all the cruel misadventures that had befallen him, Candide would not have ended up happily cultivating his garden, 'eating candied citrons and pistachio nuts', the innocent hero agrees that everything is still for the best in 'this best of all possible worlds'. When Kurt Vonnegut's Billy Pilgrim, caught up in the horrors of the Second World War, stops 'politely' in the dead centre of an open road to give a sniper 'another chance' – 'It was his addled understanding of the rules of warfare that the marksman *should* be given a second chance' – the next shot (aimed intelligently at his predicted position) 'missed his kneecaps by inches': had Billy behaved as he should, and *not* politely stopped, it would, of course, have killed him.

These are classic instances of the triumph of the absurd, which in its workings sometimes favours the innocent. Even as their mishaps, disasters and misfortunes reveal the world to be as unpredictable, capricious and irrational as it truly is, these blithely ingenuous souls persist in believing that there is an order to things, whatever it may be. For there to be no certainty, even of the time as given by the clock, is the definitive condition of absurdity, though it is a condition of neither stupidity or folly. 'Knowing the time of day' is a metaphor for sanity, but it was Einstein (no less) who told us that no two clocks tell the same time.

We have learned to live with the knowledge that our certainties are conditional, and that every guide to reality is but a device to measure the relativity of contingency to certainty. Dr. Clock's Handbook is offered as a practical corrective to solemn over-certainty, about the time or anything else.

MEL GOODING

INTRODUCTION

Almost everyday we see something that demands a reaction of surprise. For example, while crossing the road at a zebra crossing you trip over a hedgehog who is also using the zebra crossing. Providing you only trip and don't fall over, you'll reach the other side of the road and have the opportunity to reflect on what the hedgehog was doing using a crossing clearly designed for human beings. Hedgehogs usually cross any-old-where and end up squashed on the tarmac as a result. How come this fellow is behaving so absurdly? Is he copying human behaviour, as parrots imitate human speech, or consciously campaigning for equal rights for all mammals? And how exactly do hedgehogs rate zebra crossings? Why am I spouting absurdities? The absurd should not be spouted, but created and to do that you have to know the recipe, what the absurd is made of.

All absurdity arises out of an over-abundance of order. One might assume that orderly people create order and disorderly people – disorder. However, history has often proved the opposite. Disorderly folk have tried to construct a form of order from which orderly folk have tried to escape. Furthermore, attempts to classify the various forms and types of absurdity, in other words to turn absurdity into a science, only increase the density of absurdity in our lives, which pleases me no end.

"Designer" absurdity can, of course, be the subject of study, systematisation and analysis, but only when the study is limited to the work of one particular absurdist or a group who share a common ideology. I was brought up on two completely independent systems of the absurd: one being Soviet Reality, the other the work of Daniil Kharms, which was officially labelled as socially dangerous. The inquisitive old women who, one after another, tumble out of Kharms's open apartment block windows were a premonition of the desperate fight between official absurdity and unofficial absurdity. In Soviet life, instead of nosey old ladies, it was writers who did not wish to describe the official absurdity who fell out of the 'window' of Soviet official life, Kharms among them. Could it be that the secret Stalinist Tribunal had found him guilty of the premeditated murder of curious old ladies? We'll never know. He went for a walk in the forest one day in 1937 and was never seen again. It has to be said that 1937 was a particularly bad year for taking walks in Soviet forests.

Kharms could have agreed to serve the real Soviet absurdity. He could have written a novel about how ten brave old ladies built communism. Then he may well have won a state prize, instead of a stunted biography as a talented victim of the Soviet regime. Indeed a state prize for Kharms would have been the height of absurdity!

The concept of absurdity as an aesthetic category arose only relatively recently, at the end of the nineteenth century. The cultural cocktail under the title "the absurd" in which the beautiful mingled with the disgusting, the sublime with the ridiculous, the terrible with the amusing, turned out to be a very effective antidote to "common sense".

During the 1930s and 40s Nabokov became an unexpected champion of the absurd, dedicating a lecture to the subject: "Literary Art and Common Sense". Nabokov understood the absurd to be the irrational which lies beyond the reach of rational, logical thought, as opposed to "common sense", i.e. the rational. The existence of the absurd in a creative person and in what he creates, according to Nabokov, actually fertilises the soil from which new ideas spring forth.

However, life has changed a great deal since Nabokov's time. We no longer need fear "the infection of common sense" or the expansion of the absurd because it now blends harmoniously with our lives. While I am writing this introduction, some Frenchman is considering opening a Tango club in Kabul, while some other more serious thinker, busy with the government of Turkmenistan is ordering the local senior citizens to return their pension money to the state and to see if they can live on nothing. I am sure the work of Turkmenbashi (Father of all Turkmens being his official title) will appear as an entry in a future handbook of absurdity, but for now I suggest you dive into the world of absurdists from the recent past. There is something to learn from them. Their attitude to life cannot but inspire optimism and cheerfulness in the reader. For each person, and especially those interested in politics, is a potential creator of the absurd, even if he or she considers themselves to be a creator of order.

Absurdity should not be feared. For one thing it is everywhere. Secondly it will always win. At the very least it refreshes our view of life and it could win our hearts and turn us into defenders of all things irrational; after all, the rational no longer has any power to surprise.

ANDREY KURKOV

From *The Dividend*,
USA, 1916

1

ABOUT THE HOUSE

On entering the kitchen, invariably say

"Good morning, Cook"

From Mrs Beeton's *Everyday Cookery and Housekeeping Book,* 1865

IN THE KITCHEN

Two Apprehensive Eyes Scan the Recipe Book, attributed to Willi Ruge. Germany c.1933

from *The Cedilla Cookbook*

cédillic:

 6 pounds of zebra
 18 pounds of dolphin
 4 pounds of lynx
 9 tame dormice
 2 owls
 5 liters of whale oil
 dandelion root
 willow leaves

herbs

 garam masala
 powdered fresh coffee
 palm tree kernels
 cactus hearts

 ocean water
 river water

Put the ocean water in a large caldron over the fire. Disembowel and clean the animals, whose variety must be as great as possible, and who give their best flavor when they have just been caught, and not waiting in captivity. Clean the dandelion root and the willow leaves. Throw into the boiling water the animals cut into small pieces, add the whale oil, dandelion root and willow leaves, the garam masala, powdered coffee, palm tree kernels, and cactus hearts. Let simmer on a slow fire for several days, adding river water if necessary. Pour the bouillon on tortillas and serve the meat in a hollow plate, or serve them both together. It is possible to make the dish even more tasty by adding, first, one little pickle cut in slices; second, geranium petals (vigorously wash them before parting them). They will be added to the dish two seconds before serving.

Serves:
 2 Vostells
 39 Brechts
 1000 Maciunases
 8 Dick Higginses
 1 Emmett Williams

From *Games at the Cedilla, or the Cedilla Takes Off*, George Brecht and Robert Filliou, 1967

Sian Bonnell, *Beanfeast*, 2002

COOKING ON YOUR CAR ENGINE

SALMON TAMWORTH PERRY-SMITH

Prepare as for Salmon in Pastry with Herb Sauce (Jane Grigson, Fish Cookery, p.223), but replace pastry with triple-wrapped foil. Wire onto a hot exhaust manifold (eg. after driving from Lanark to Biggar) of a Reliant Scimitar with a small air-filter, and drive approximately 15 miles.

FOUR FROM SEVEN

4 red peppers, blanched
1 red chilli
6 cloves of garlic
8 dried apricots plus 2 oz chopped
1 onion
4oz chopped mushrooms plus 4 whole ones
2oz chopped tomato
3oz chopped nuts
1 tbs olive oil
salt, pepper
oregano
tomato puree

Stuff peppers architecturally and wrap in two packages of 15 layers of foil. Bind with wire coathangers, leaving hooks free. Suspend one parcel between the exhaust pipes of a Carterham Super seven, hanging from the oil-cooling pipes, and clamp the other to the 4th cylinder. This is the only position which will not vaporise the foil. Drive as dynamically as possible around country roads for 30 miles.

SCIMITAR SPICED PORK

2 pork fillets cut into 1 cm dice
bunch of syboes (spring onions)
2 onions
100g button mushrooms
1 green capsicum
a piece of fresh ginger root

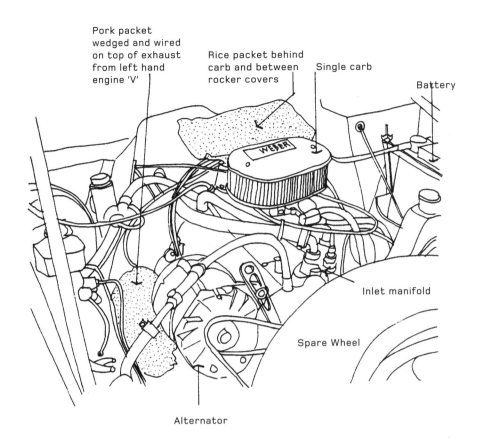

Pork packet wedged and wired on top of exhaust from left hand engine 'V'

Rice packet behind carb and between rocker covers

Single carb

Battery

Inlet manifold

Spare Wheel

Alternator

Marinade the pork overnight in a mixture of sesame oil and dark soy sauce. Next day, prepare syboes and mushrooms; slice onions and capsicum; cut the ginger into julienne strips and blanch to taste. Drain the meat, then stir-fry briefly, adding the vegetables for the last minute of cooking. Season and commit to triple-layered foil, with the added precaution of a pad foil on the side of the package destined to sit on the manifold. The package should be about 12 cm by 20, and can be tightly wrapped. If desired, it can be cooled and refrigerated at this point.

The Scimitar has a Ford 2.8 litre V-6 engine, but in order to cook on it a reduced-size K&N air filter has to be fitted, otherwise there is no room for the food. This is a super engine to cook on. Because it has a V formation, there are exhaust manifold on either side of the block, both of which can be used for cooking. Then there are warm spaces on top of the air-filter and in a special little plate-warming space right at the back, nearest the dashboard. Wire the food into position, and drive for 30 miles at speeds varying from 25 to as fast as you can.

From *The One! The Only! Guide to Cooking on Your Car Engine*, Chris Maynard and Bill Scheller, 1989

ON SUNDAYS IT WAS MY JOB
TO PREPARE A PICNIC LUNCH
USING MOTHER'S HOME-BAKED
WHOLEMEAL BREAD....

From Glen Baxter, *His Life: the Years of Struggle*, 1983

Werner Hauser, *Noblesse Oblige*, (models: Max and Hedula) 1975

THE JOYS OF SEX

From *The Measurement of Social Competence: A Manual for the Vineland Social Maturity Scale,* 1953

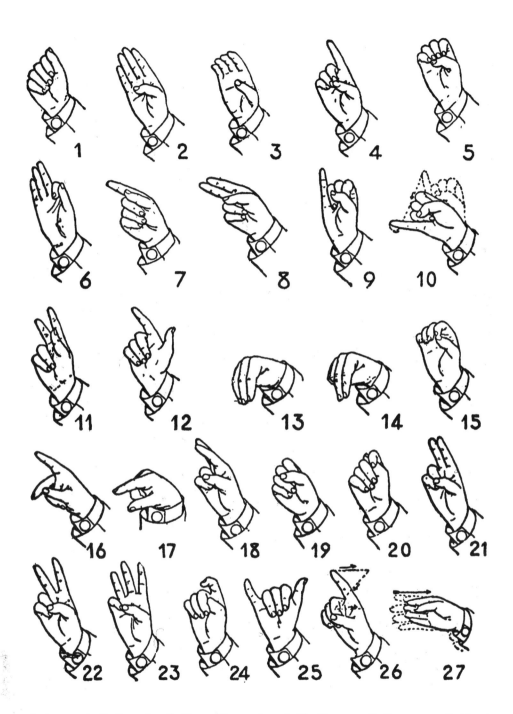

1: Accost 2: Burgle 3: Cunnilinguate 4: Deflower 5: Ensnare 6: Fuck
7: Gallivant 8: Harass 9: Irrumate 10: Jismify 11: Kink 12: Lesbianise
13: Masturbate 14: Nidify 15: Occult 16: Pedicate 17: Quench 18: Ream
19: Syphilize 20: Tup 21: Urticate 22: Violate 23: Waggle 24: Xiphoidify
25: Yonirise 26: Zoogonise 27: Recommence

From *The Da Costa Encyclopedia,* anonymously and collectively edited, 1947

Maurizio Cattelan, *Not Afraid of Love*, 2000

ob Watts and George Maciunas, *Underpants Implosions Inc. with Maciunas,* 1967

Saul Steinberg, *Dancing Couple,* 1965

TABLE IV—INCIDENCE OF EXTRA-MARITAL SEXUAL ACTIVITY REPORTED BY MARRIED, SEPARATED, DIVORCED AND WIDOWED ARTISTS (BY AGE GROUPS)

Age Group	Extra-marital Coitus Among Artists with Histories of Pre-marital Coitus	Exrta-marital Coitus Among Artists with No Histories of Pre-marital Coitus
18 and 19	9%	11%
20 to 24	22	24
25 to 29	23	27
30 to 34	26	29
35 to 39	28	31
40 to 44	29	33
45 to 49	31	36
50 to 54	29	31
55 to 59	27	26
60 to 64	24	23
65 and over	23%	21%

Notes: 1. Ages are those at time of interview.
2. All percentages to nearest whole percent.

TABLE V—PRE-MARITAL AND EXTRA-MARITAL SEXUAL PARTNERS OF ARTISTS ADMITTING TO PRE-MARITAL AND/OR EXTRA-MARITAL COITAL EXPERIENCES

Partners with whom Artists Engaged in Pre- or Extra-marital Sex Activities	Pre-marital Coitus	Extra-marital Coitus
Artists and/or dealers only	11%	21%
Critics only	13	6
Other than artists, dealers or critics only	28	24
Artists and/or dealers and critics only	6	8
Artists and/or dealers and other than critics only	9	15
Critics and other than artists and dealers only	12	9
All three categories	21	17
TOTALS	100%	100%

Note: All percentages shown are to nearest whole percent.

From *Games at the Cedilla, or the Cedilla Takes Off,* George Brecht and Robert Filliou, 1967

TABLE VI—NUMBER OF DIFFERENT PRE-MARITAL AND EXTRA-MARITAL PARTNERS REPORTED BY ARTISTS

Number of Different Partners	Pre-marital Coitus	Extra-marital Coitus
One only (See note 1)	48%	34%
2 to 5	36	37
6 to 9	11	16
10 to 19	4	9
20 or more (See note 2)	1	4
TOTALS	100%	100%

Notes: 1. In pre-marital coitus column, 48% figure includes 26% of artists who had pre-marital intercourse only with the person they later married.
2. Maximum number of partners reported was stated as "at least 100 different men a year since I was 19" by a 26-year-old paintress. This figure, of course, may be exaggerated.
3. All percentages shown to nearest whole percent.

TABLE VII—INCIDENCE OF HOMOSEXUALITY AMONG ARTISTS

Artists Having:	AGE GROUPS				
	18 to 24	25 to 34	35 to 44	45 to 54	55 and over
NO homosexual contacts	87%	83%	81%	79%	81%
ONE homosexual contact	9	10	11	12	9
TWO to FIVE homosexual contacts	2	4	4	3	3
More than FIVE homosexual contacts	1	2	2	3	3
Characterizing themselves confirmed homosexuals	1	1	2	3	4
TOTALS	100%	100%	100%	100%	100%

Notes: 1. Readers might be interested to note that artists' homosexual incidence rate is generally well below levels reported by Kinsey. (See *Sexual Behavior in the Human Female*, W. B. Saunders & Co., 1953, Ch. 11.)
2. All percentages shown are to nearest whole percent.
3. Ages are those at time of interview.

TABLE VIII—DRUG HABITS OF ARTISTS

Population Where Artist Lives	Total Abstainers	Light	Moderate	Heavy	Very Heavy
Rural Areas	26%	37%	23%	9%	5%
Under 25,000	22	47	21	7	3
25,000 to 100,000	14	52	23	8	3
100,000 to 500,000	12	44	32	8	4
Over 500,000	11%	35%	41%	9%	4%

Notes: 1. Data is based on artists' own descriptions of amount of drug taking.
2. All percentages in each category total 100.
3. All percentages shown are to nearest whole percent.

TABLE IX—INCIDENCE OF GROUP SEX AMONG ARTISTS

Artists Having:	
No group sex	92%
Occasional group sex	7
Permanent group sex	1
TOTAL	100%

Note: Readers might be interested to know that for the members of La Cédille Qui Sourit, the group sex incidence is 100%.

Sergei Eisenstein in Mexico, 1930. Photographer unknown

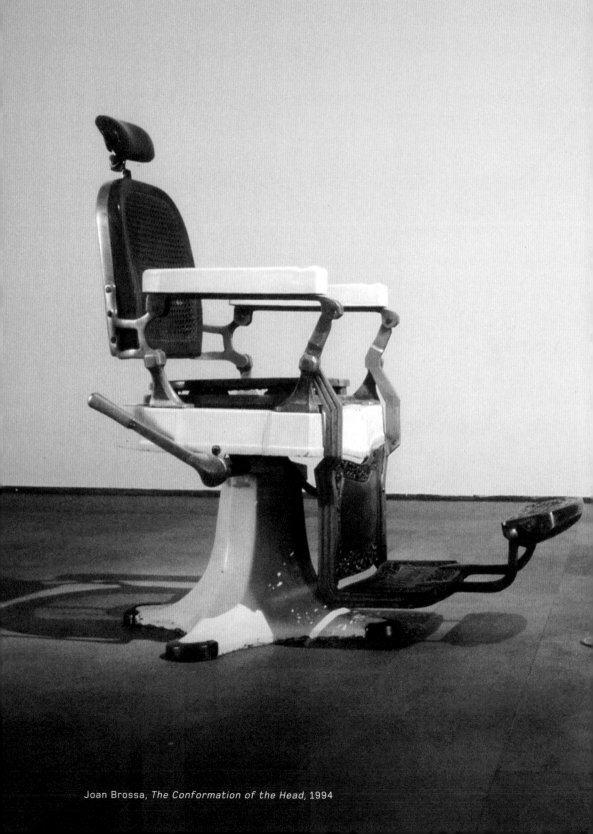

Joan Brossa, *The Conformation of the Head*, 1994

Colours for identification, coding and special purposes.*

283	Spartacus	389	Orson Welles	593	Ferdinand & Imelda Marcos
285	Malcolm X	410	Jules Verne	626	Ferdinand & Isabella
298	Niccolo Machiavelli	411	Josephus	627	Isabella Rossellini
309	Tzar Nicholas II	412	Empress Josephine	630	Ingrid Bergman
310	Nat Turner	414	Napoleon Bonaparte	631	John Coltrane
320	J.M.W. Turner	436	Maximilien de Robespierre	632	John Major
337	Kathleen Turner	437	Bobby Robson	637	John Paul Jones
352	John Constable	445	Flora Robson	638	Michael Collins
353	John Paul Getty	447	Florence Nightingale	641	William Burroughs
355	Johnny Cash	454	Valerie Solanas	642	Edgar Rice Burroughs
356	Fidel Castro	499	Cassius Clay	676	Edgar Allan Poe
358	Brigitte Bardot	537	B.B. King	677	Marco Polo
361	Jane Russell	538	Rosso Fiorentino	692	Daniel Defoe
363	Sir James Young Simpson	539	Mantegna	693	Sean Connery, George Lazen
365	David Livingstone	541	Rajiv Gandhi		Roger Moore & Timothy Dalt
367	William Wilberforce	542	Mary Magdelene	694	Don Diego de Silva y Velazqu
368	Giuseppe Verdi	557	Judge Clarence Thomas	697	Cardinal Richelieu
369	Sir Arthur Conan Doyle	564	Professor Anita Hill	796	Richard the Third
384	Basil Rathbone	568	Thomas Mann	797	Ethelred the Unready
388	H.G. Wells	592	Judge Jeffreys		

*This series of colours corresponds to B.S. 381C, published by the British Standards Institute, in 1988. (This series does not include the twenty five 'obsolescent' colours in B.S.381C)

- The colours in this series are available in Matt, Vinyl Silk, Gloss and Eggshell finish.
- Paint is available in the following sizes;

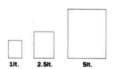

1lt. 2.5lt. 5lt.

Each paint is available to order up to a maximum quantity of 10 litres (e.g. 10x1lt., 4x2.5lt., 2x5lt.), the minimum order being 1 litre. Note – Each paint number/name will be available to one person only.

B.S.***   B.S.***   B.S.***
Tito Gobbi   Maria Callas   Jimmy Carter

ORDER FORM

	Finish		Quantity		CONTACT:
MATT	☐	1 LITRE	☐	£80.00+p&p	GLASGOW: DOUGLAS GORDON
					(OFFICE) c/o REDSTONE PRE
VINYL SILK	☐	2.5 LITRES	☐	£100.00+p&p	
					LONDON: SIMON PATTERSON
GLOSS	☐	5 LITRES	☐	£150.00+p&p	(DESPATCH) c/o REDSTONE PRE
EGGSHELL	☐		PAINT NAME/NUMBER		

Simon Patterson and Douglas Gordon, *Project for Frieze Magazine,* 1991

RIGHT: The Marx Brothers

Richard Wentworth, from the series *Making Do and Getting By*, 1995

Buster Keaton looks at the house he has assembled in *One Week*, 1920

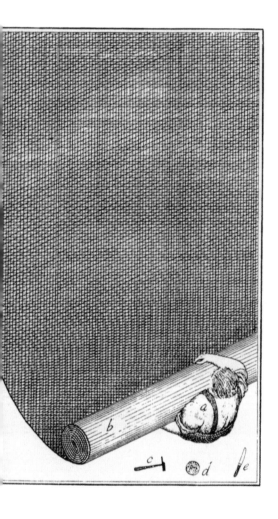

ques Carelman, LEFT: THE CARPETLAYER, a) the carpet, b) the roll of carpet, c) the carpet hammer
he carpet tacks e) the carpet knife RIGHT: THE CARPET IN POSITION

Blue Car in Cyprus, photograph by Piers Wardle, 1998

Fence designer Graham Armstrong inspects his masterpiece   Photo: National Parks Board

The Marquis of Bath relaxing, c.1968

AT HOME

THE PLEASURES OF THE DOOR

Kings never touch doors.

They're not familiar with this happiness: to push, gently or roughly before you one of these great, friendly panels, to turn towards it to put it back in place – to hold a door in your arms.

The happiness of seizing one of these small barriers to a room by the porcelain knob of its belly; this quick hand-to-hand, during which your progress slows for a moment, your eye opens up and your whole body adapts to its new apartment.

With a friendly hand you hold on a bit longer, before firmly pushing it back and shutting yourself in – of which you are agreeably assured by the click of the powerful, well-oiled latch.

FRANCIS PONGE

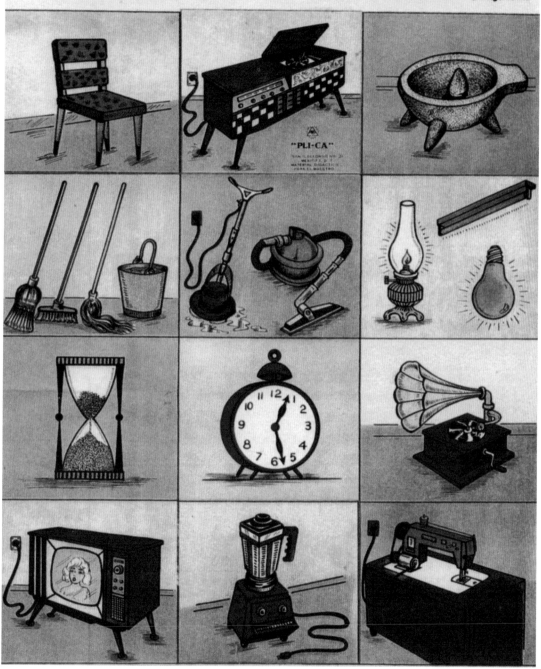

Objects for the home, Mexican wall chart, 1960s

OVERLEAF: Sian Bonnell, *Beach Clean*, 1999

Here are the men of the family hard at it. The boy has reached an age when he likes to copy father in everything—and he's delighted to have a real cable pullover made to the same pattern as father's.

From *Knitting for All*, 1947

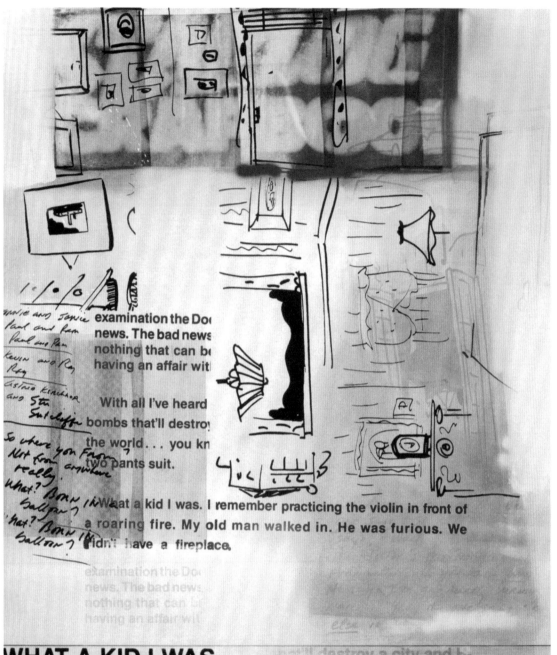

examination the Do(
news. The bad news
nothing that can be
having an affair wit

With all I've heard
bombs that'll destro
the world . . . you kn
two pants suit.

What a kid I was. I remember practicing the violin in front of
a roaring fire. My old man walked in. He was furious. We
didn't have a fireplace.

WHAT A KID I WAS.
I remember practicing the violin in front
of a roaring fire. My old man walked in.
He was furious. We didn't have a fireplace.

Richard Prince, *What A Kid I Was*, 1988

Cornelia Parker, *Cold Dark Matter:
An Exploded View (detail of Blown-up
hot-water bottle)*, 1991

2

OUT AND ABOUT

THIS DOES NOT WORK

I can't turn the heating on / off

The lock is broken

I can't open the window

The toilet won't flush

There is no hot water

The washbasin is dirty

The room is noisy / dark

My coffee is cold

We are still waiting

I bought this here yesterday

It has a hole in it

Collins Portuguese Phrasebook and Dictionary, 1990
From *Conversation Guide* by Pavel Büchler (work in progress)

FROM THE BOOK OF DISQUIET

The only real traveller with soul that I've known was an office boy at another firm where I was once employed. This young fellow collected promotional brochures for cities, countries and transportation companies; he had maps that he'd torn out of journals or that he'd asked for here and there; he had illustrations of landscapes, prints of exotic costumes, and pictures of boats and ships that he'd clipped out of newspapers and magazines. He would go to travel agencies in the name of some imaginary office, or perhaps in the name of a real office, perhaps even the one where he worked, and he would ask for brochures about trips to Italy, brochures about excursions to India, brochures listing the boat connections between Portugal and Australia.

He was not only the greatest - because truest - traveller I've known, he was also one of the happiest people I've had the privilege to meet. I regret not knowing what's become of him, or rather, I pretend I should regret it; in fact I don't, because by now, ten years or more after the brief period when I knew him, he must be a grown-up, a responsible idiot who fulfils his duties, perhaps as a married man, somebody's provider - dead, that is, while still alive. And maybe he has even travelled in body, he who travelled so well in his soul.

I just remembered: he knew the exact route of the train from Paris to Bucharest as well as the routes of all the trains in England, and as he mispronounced the strange names, I could see the glowing certainty of his greatness of soul. Today, yes, he probably exists as a dead man, but perhaps one day, in his old age, he will remember how it's not only better but also truer to dream of Bordeaux than to actually go there.

FERNANDO PESSOA

Nina Katchadourian, *Coastal Merger* (designed to make it quicker to drive coast to coast), 1995

Les Coleman, 1978

FACT/FICTION AND THE AIRPORT

1) Visit the airport bookstand and buy a book at random.

2) Pick out the name of a minor character and write it down in large block

capitals on a piece of white card.

3) Wait at the Arrivals gate until you are approached by that person and

witness fiction reverting back to fact again.

1) Take the title of the same book and ask for it to be translated from English

to Spanish at the London-Madrid check-in desk.

2) Give the translated title to a passenger, asking them to find a translation

into Arabic at the Madrid-Cairo check-in desk.

3) Make certain someone in Cairo asks for a Russian translation at the Cairo-

Moscow desk.

4) Wait at the Arrivals gate for the Chinese-English translation.

(This process can be applied to entire novels.)

From *An A to Z for the Effective Use of Your City* by Adam Dant (Donald Parsnips), Atlas Press, 1999

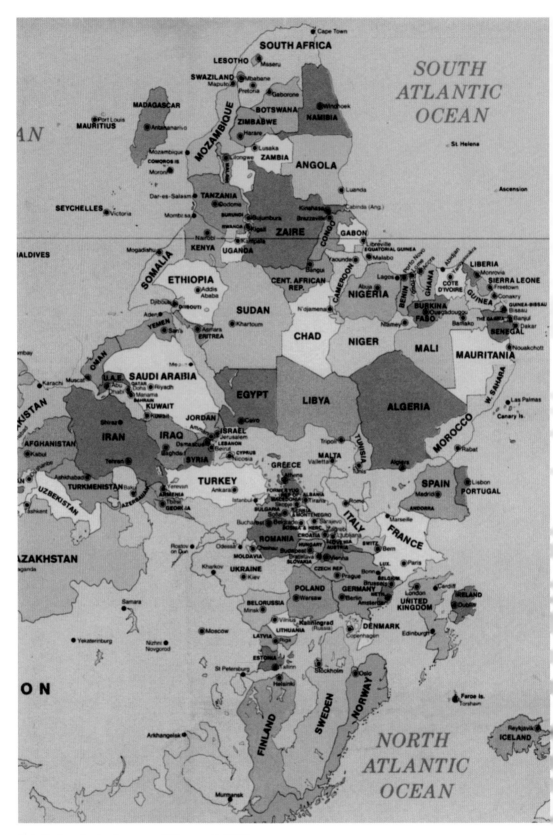

Detail of an Australian map of the world, 1990

ON THE DIFFICULTY OF IMAGINING AN IDEAL CITY

I wouldn't like to live in America but sometimes I would

I'd love to live on the Boulevard St-Germain but sometimes I wouldn't

I wouldn't like to live on a coral reef but sometimes I would

I wouldn't like to live in a dungeon but sometimes I would

I wouldn't like to live in the East but sometimes I would

I love living in France but sometimes I don't

I'd love to live in Greenland but not for too long

I'd like to live to a hundred but sometimes I wouldn't

I wouldn't like to live in Issoudun but sometimes I would

I wouldn't like to live on a junk but sometimes I would

I wouldn't like to live in a ksar but sometimes I would

I'd have loved to go in a lunar module but it's a bit late

I wouldn't like to live in a monastery but sometimes I would

I wouldn't like to live at the Hotel Negresco but sometimes I would

I wouldn't like to live in the open air but sometimes I would

I love living in Paris but sometimes I don't

I wouldn't like to live in Quebec but sometimes I would

I wouldn't like to live by my own resources but sometimes I would

I wouldn't like to live in a submarine but sometimes I would

I wouldn't like to live in a tower but sometimes I would

I wouldn't like to live with Ursula Andress but sometimes I would

I wouldn't like to live in a village but sometimes I would

I wouldn't like to live in a wigwam but sometimes I would

I'd love to live in Xanadu but not for ever

I wouldn't like to live in the Yonne but sometimes I would

I wouldn't like us all to live in Zanzibar but sometimes I would

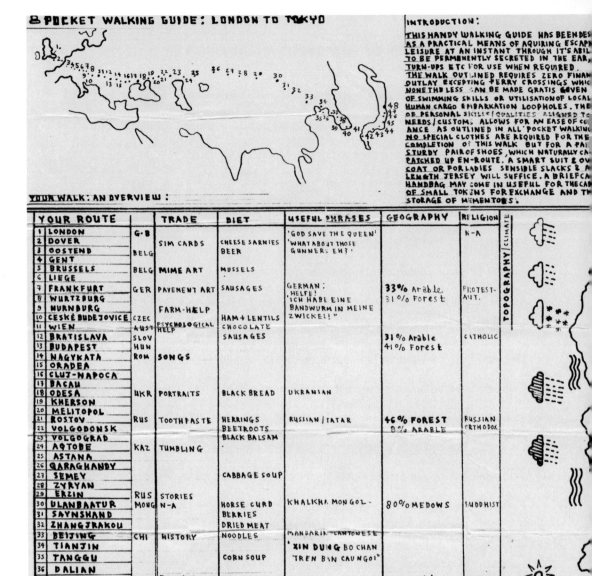

Adam Dant, *Donald Parsnips Pocket Walking Guide: London to Tokyo*

Michael Stern, Concrete tepees (holiday village), USA, 1980

Douglas Gordon, *Psycho Hitchhiker*, 1993

FRANZ KAFKA: THREE SHORT STORIES

GIVE IT UP!

It was very early in the morning, the streets clean and deserted, I was on my way to the station. As I compared the tower clock with my watch I realized it was much later than I had thought and that I had to hurry; the shock of this discovery made me feel uncertain of the way, I wasn't very well acquainted with the town as yet; fortunately, there was a policeman at hand, I ran to him and breathlessly asked him the way. He smiled and said: "You asking me the way?" "Yes," I said, "since I can't find it myself." "Give it up! Give it up!" said he, and turned with a sudden jerk, like someone who wants to be alone with his laughter.

THE DEPARTURE

I ordered my horse to be brought from the stables. The servant did not understand my orders. So I went to the stables myself, saddled my horse, and mounted. In the distance I heard the sound of a trumpet, and I asked the servant what it meant. He knew nothing and had heard nothing. At the gate he stopped me and asked: "Where is the master going?" "I don't know," I said, "just out of here, just out of here. Out of here, nothing else, it's the only way I can reach my goal." "So you know your goal?" he asked. "Yes," I replied, "I've just told you. Out of here – that's my goal."

THE NEXT VILLAGE

My grandfather used to say: "Life is astoundingly short. To me, looking back over it, life seems so foreshortened that I scarcely understand, for instance, how a young man can decide to ride over to the next village without being afraid that – not to mention accidents – even the span of a normal happy life may fall far short of the time needed for such a journey."

ENGLISH AS SHE IS SPOKE
FROM THE NEW GUIDE OF THE CONVERSATION IN PORTUGUESE AND ENGLISH

Senhor Pedro Carolino first published his indispensable Guide in 1855 in Paris. Its ineffable absurdity derives from a perfectly logical premise: that it should be possible to compile a guide book to a language unknown to the compiler by means of reference works in an intermediary language. Carolino's *'choice of familiar dialogues, clean of gallicisms, and despoiled phrases'* was put together, it must be assumed, using a Portuguese-French phrase book and an English-French dictionary. Supremely confident of its success, Carolino prefaced his book with criticism of existing 'Works' which he consulted and *'fond use us for nothing'*: the *'carelessness to rest these Works fill of imperfections, and anomalies of style; in spite of the infinite typographic faults which some times, invert the sense of periods.'* He is confident that, free of these imperfections, his own *'little book (for care of what we wrote him, and for her typographical correction) that may be worth the acceptation of the studious persons, and especialy of the Youth, at which we dedicate him particularly.'*

Carolino's 'English' is not without its own strange and surprising poetry, unimaginable without the inadvertent transformations effected by its method. The application of its logic creates a kind of unconscious through which the ordinary and the everyday is transmuted into the pure gold of inspired nonsense. Imagine a play written by one of Senhor Carolino's more assiduously studious persons: the ultimate in absurd drama. (MG)

USEFUL WORDS

OF THE MAN
The brain
The brains
The fat of the leg
The ham
The inferior lip
The superior lip
The marrow
The reins

DEFECTS OF THE BODY
A blind
A lame
A bald
A left handed
An ugly
A squint-eyed
A deaf

EATINGS
Some black pudding
Some sugar-plum
Some wigs

A chitterling sausages
A dainty-dishes
A mutton shoulder
A little mine
Hog fat
Some marchpanes
An amelet
A slice, steak
Vegetables boiled to a pap

WOMAN OBJECTS
The busk
The sash
The cornet
The pumps
The paint or disguise
The patches
The skate

DISEASES
The apoplexy
The scrofulas
The melancholy

The megrime
The whitlow
The rheumatisme
The vomitory

CHIVALRY ORDERS
Black eagle
Avis, advice
Calatrava
Elephant
Honour Legion
Saint Michaelmas
Very-merit

GAMES
Foot-ball
Bar
Gleek
Carousal
Pile
Mall
Even or non even
Keel

NATURAL HISTORY

INSECTS-REPTILES
Asp, aspic
Morpian
Fly
Butter Fly
Serpent

QUADRUPED'S BEASTS
Lamb
Ass
Shi ass
Ram, aries
Dragon
Wild sow
Lioness
Rocbuck
Dormouse

BIRDS
Becafico
Calander
Star
Yeung turkey
Heuth-cock
Whoop
Pea cock
Pinch
Red-breast, a robin.

FISHES AND SHELL-FISHES
Calamary
Dorado
A sorte of fish
Hedge hog
Large lobster
Snail
Wolf
Torpedo
Sea-calf

FAMILIAR PHRASES

Have you say that?
Have you understand that he says?
At what purpose have say so?
Dress your hairs.
Sing an area.
These apricots and these peaches make
      me and to come water in mouth.
That is what I have think.
This ink is white.
This room is filled of bugs.
This girl have a beauty edge.
This wood is fill of thief's.
Will you and take a walk with me?
Go through that meadow. Who the
      country is beautiful! who
      the trees are thick!
You hear the bird's gurgling?
Which pleasure! which charm!
Are you hunter? will you go to the hunting
      in one day this week?
Willingly; I have not a most pleasure in the
      world.
Dry this wine.
He laughs at my nose, he jest by me.
He has spit in my coat.
He has me take out my hairs.
He does me some kicks.
He do the devil at four.
He make to weep the room.

It must never to laugh of the unhappies.
I am confused all yours civilities.
I have croped the candle.
I have mind to vomit.
Have you understanded?

IDIOTISMS AND PROVERBS

The necessity don't know the low.
Few, few the bird make her nest.
Its are some blu stories.
He sin in trouble water.
Take out the live coals with the hand
      of the cat.
A horse baared don't look him the tooth.
Take the occasion for the hairs.
To do a wink to some body.
Which like Bertram, love hir dog.
The stone as roll not heap up not foam.
They shurt him the doar in face.
He has fond the knuckle of the business.
He is beggar as a church rat.
Keep the chestnut of the fire with the
      cat foot.
Burn the politeness.
After the paunch comes the dance.
To craunch the marmoset.
To fatten the foot.

Sian Bonnell, *Scenic Cookery*, 2003

London Underground

Tube map

February 2006

DAVID SHRIGLEY

MAYOR OF LONDON · **Transport for London** ·

David Shrigley, *Map of the London Underground*, 2005

EVERYDAY LIFE

AN ENCOUNTER

On one occasion a man went off to work and on the way he met another man who, having bought a loaf of Polish bread, was wending his way home.

And that's just about all there is to it.

DANIIL KHARMS

Indian Cinema poster, 1970s

Ed Ruscha, *20th Century*, 1987

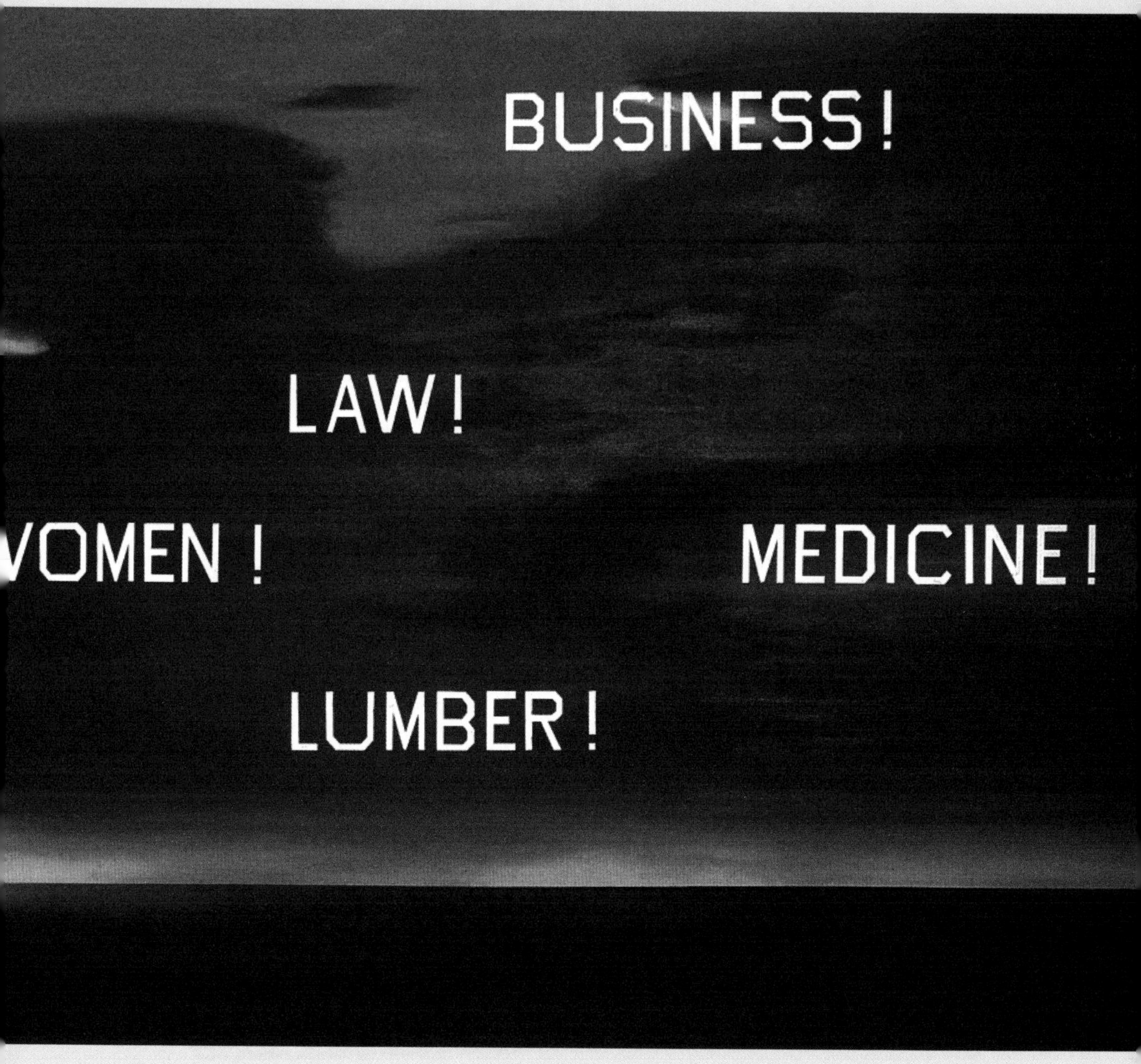
BUSINESS!
LAW!
VOMEN!
MEDICINE!
LUMBER!

Engraving by J.G.Posada, Mexico, c. 1895

THE PLUMMETING OLD WOMEN

A certain old woman, out of excessive curiosity, fell out of a window, plummeted to the ground, and was smashed to pieces.

Another old woman leaned out of the window and began looking at the remains of the first one, but she also, out of excessive curiosity, fell out of the window, plummeted to the ground and was smashed to pieces.

Then a third old woman plummeted from the window, then a fourth, then a fifth.

By the time a sixth old woman had plummeted down, I was fed up watching them, and went off to Mal'tseviskiy Market where, it was said, a knitted shawl had been given to a certain blind man.

DANIIL KHARMS

He who bestirs himself is lost

Never wait for yourself

The further the urn the longer the beard

Cold meat lights no fire

A crab, by any other name, would not forget the sea

I came, I sat, I departed

Who hears but me hears all

Proverbs by Paul Eluard and Benjamin Péret, 1925

NUTS IN MARCH

On 13 March 1977, Mr Alfred Wilson Osborne (a chess correspondent for a newspaper) and his wife were on their way back from church near their home in Bristol when they experienced what Mr Osborne describes as 'a most amazing thing'. They were passing a large car saleroom when, according to Osborne, 'there was a click as if I'd lost a button, and I realized that it was not a button which I had lost, but something had fallen from the sky.' That 'something' was a hazelnut, and at once the Osbornes found themselves caught in a whole shower of them: they estimate that there were between 350 and 400. 'They were just pinging on the cars as they went down,' says Mrs Osborne. To be caught in a shower of hazelnuts on a Sunday morning in Bristol at any time would be strange enough, but not only were there no nut trees in the road, but hazelnuts are not in season until September or October – and this was March. 'Yet', says Mr Osborne, 'they were quite fresh and sweet and nice.' Moreover, the Osbornes are certain the nuts were not thrown in some way from the flat roof of the nearby car saleroom: they were coming from the sky, which was 'practically clear and blue with one cloud drifting over'.

In the hope of solving the mystery, Mr Osborne kept a few of the nuts and told his friends about the shower; but, he says, 'the first reaction I got was that I was nuts like the hazels.' One of the Osbornes' friends, however, also walked through the falling nuts, when he passed the car saleroom about three minutes later, but neither he, nor the readers of the local newspaper to whom Mr Osborne turned for help, could provide an explanation. 'It's impossible to account for it, actually', says Mr Osborne. 'How they came and where they came from, I have no idea, but I have thought that it might be a vortex sucked them up, but I don't know where you suck up hazelnuts in March.'

Wilson Osborne and his wife standing where they were showered with nuts.

From *Arthur C. Clarke's Mysterious World*, by Arthur C. Clarke, Simon Welfare and John Fairley, 1985

Wim Delvoye, *Bell is broken, please knock, Tina*, 2000

Delvoye, *David, just popped out for a moment, back in 10 mins.*, 1997

What I see, what I see. What I see is the day in all its absurdity and triviality. A horse, harnessed to a cab, staring with lowered head into its nose bag, not knowing that horses originally came into the world without cabs; a small boy playing with marbles on the pavement - he watches the purposeful bustle of the grownups all around him, and, himself full of the delights of idleness has no inkling that he already represents the acme of creation, but instead yearns to be grown up; a policeman who fancies himself as the still point at the centre of a whirlpool of activity, and the pillar of authority - enemy to the street, and placed there to supervise it and accept its tribute in the form of good order.

I see a girl, framed in an open window, who is a part of the wall and yearns to be freed from its embrace, which is all she knows of the world. A man, pressed into the shadows of a public square, collecting bits of paper and cigarette butts. An advertising kiosk placed at the head of a street, like its epigram, with a little weathervane on it to proclaim which way the wind is blowing down that particular street. A fat man in a cream-coloured jacket, smoking a cigar, he looks like a grease spot in human form on this summer's day. A café terrace planted with colourful ladies, waiting to be plucked. White-jacketed waiters, navy blue porters, newspaper sellers, a hotel, an elevator boy, a Negro.

What I see is the old man with the tin trumpet on the Kurfürstendamm. He is a beggar whose plight draws all the more attention to itself for being inaudible. Sometimes the falsetto of the little tin trumpet is stronger and more powerful than the entire Kurfürstendamm. And the motion of a waiter on the café terrace, swishing at a fly, has more content in it than the lives of all the customers on the café terrace. The fly gets away, and the waiter is disappointed. Why so much hostility to a fly, O waiter? A war cripple who finds a nail file. Someone, a lady, has lost the nail file in the place where he happens to sit down. Of course the beggar starts filing his nails - what else is he to do? The coincidence that has left the nail file in his possession and the trifling movement of filing his nails are enough to lift him about a thousand social classes, symbolically speaking. A dog running after a ball, then stopping in front of it, static now and inanimate - unable to grasp how some stupid, brainless rubber thing only a moment ago could have been so lively and spirited - is the hero of a momentary drama. It's only the minutiae of life that are important.

Strolling around on a May morning, what do I care about the vast issues of world history as expressed in newspaper editorials? Or even the fate of some individual, a potential tragic hero, someone who has lost his wife or come into an inheritance or cheated on his wife or in one way or another makes some lofty appeal to us? Confronted with the truly microscopic, all loftiness is hopeless, completely meaningless. The diminutive of the parts is more impressive than the monumentality of the whole. I no longer have any use for the sweeping gestures of heroes on the global stage. I'm going for a walk.

Seeing an advertising kiosk on which facts such as, for instance, Manoli cigarettes are blazoned out as if they were an ultimatum or a *memento mori*, I completely lose my patience. An ultimatum is just as inconsequential as a cigarette, because it's expressed in exactly the same way. Whatever is heralded or touted can only be of little weight or consequence. And it seems to me there is nothing these days that is not heralded. Therein lies its greatness. Typography, to us, has become the arbiter of perspective and value. The most important, the less important, and the unimportant only *appear* to be important, less important, unimportant. It's their image that tells us their worth, not their being. The event of the week is whatever - in print, in gesture, in sweeping arm movements - has been declared the event of the week. Nothing is, everything claims to be. But in the face of the sunshine that spreads ruthlessly over walls, streets, railway tracks, beams in at the window, beams out of windows in myriad reflections, anything puffed up and inessential can have no being. In the end (led astray as I am by print, by the presence of typography as an adjudicator of value) I come to believe that everything we take seriously - the ultimatum, the Manoli cigarettes - is unimportant.

Meanwhile, at the edge of the city, where I have been told nature is to be found, it isn't nature at all, but a sort of picture-book nature. It seems to me too much has been printed about nature for it to remain what it used to be. On the outskirts of our cities, in place of nature, we are presented with a sort of idea of nature. A woman standing at the edge of the woods, shielding her eyes with the umbrella she has brought along just in case, scanning the horizon, and seeing a spot that seems familiar from some painting, exclaims: "Isn't this just so picturesque!" It's the degradation of nature to a painters' model. It's not such a rare degradation either, because our relationship to nature has become warped. You see, nature has acquired a purpose where we are concerned. Its task is to amuse us. It no longer exists for its own sake. It exists to satisfy a function. In summer it provides woods where we can picnic and doze, lakes where we can row, meadows where we can bask, sunsets to send us into raptures, mountains for walking tours, and beauty spots as destinations for our excursions and day-trips. We have Baedeker-ised nature.

But what I see hasn't made it into the Baedeker. What I see is the sudden, unexpected, and wholly meaningless rising and falling of a swarm of mosquitoes over a tree trunk. The silhouette of a man laden with firewood on a forest path. The eager profile of a spray of jasmine tumbling over a wall. The vibration of a child's voice, fading away into the air. The inaudible, sleeping melody of a distant, even an unreal life.

I don't understand the people I see putting their best foot forward to enjoy nature. There's a difference between a forest and a sidewalk. "Recreation" is no necessity, if that's the expressed objective of the hiker. "Nature" is no institution.

Western Europeans set out into nature as if to a costume party. They have a sort of waxed jacket relationship with nature. I saw hikers who were accountants in civilian life. What did they need their walking sticks for? The ground is so flat and smooth that a fountain pen would have served them just as well. But the man doesn't see the flat and smooth ground. He sees "nature." If he were going sailing, presumably he would don the white linen suit he inherited from his grandfather, who was also a weekend sailor. He has no ears for the plashing of a wave, and he doesn't know that the bursting of a bubble is a significant thing. The day that nature became a site for recreation was the end.

In consequence of which, my outing was that of a curmudgeonly soul, and I wish I hadn't undertaken it.

On the lookout! Many of you have been looking for just this type of muffler helmet. It does mean that both the head and the throat are properly protected, and the careless man can't leave his scarf behind just when he needs it most.

From *Knitting For All*, 1947

WHY?

"No one ever came out of there."

"No one?"

"No one."

"Not one?"

"No."

"Yes! And when I passed by, one nonetheless stood there."

"In front of the door?"

"In front of the door. He stood and spread his arms apart."

"Yes! It is because he doesn't want to let anyone in."

"No one went in there?"

"No one."

"That one, who spread his arms apart, was he there?"

"Inside?"

"Yes, inside."

"I don't know. He spread his hands only later, so that no one will go in there."

"They put him there so that no one will go inside there?"

"The one who spread his arms apart?"

"No. He came himself, stood there and spread his arms apart."

"And no one, no one, no one came out of there?"

"No one, no one."

WASSILY KANDINSKY

A VIEW OF THINGS

what I love about dormice is their size

what I hate about rain is its sneer

what I love about the Bratach Gorm is its unflappability

what I hate about scent is its smell

what I love about newspapers is their etaoin shrdl

what I hate about philosophy is its pursed lip

what I love about Rory is his old grouse

what I hate about Pam is her pinkie

what I love about semi-precious stones is their preciousness

what I hate about diamonds is their mink

what I love about poetry is its ion engine

what I hate about hogs is their setae

what I love about love is its porridge-spoon

what I hate about hate is its eyes

what I love about hate is its salts

what I hate about love is its dog

what I love about Hank is his string vest

what I hate about the twins is their three gloves

what I love about Mabel is her teeter

what I hate about gooseberries is their look, feel, smell and taste

what I love about the world is its shape

what I hate about a gun is its lock, stock, and barrel

what I love about bacon-and-eggs is its predictability

what I hate about derelict buildings is their reluctance to disintegrate

what I love about a cloud is its unpredictability

what I hate about you, chum, is your china

what I love about many waters is their inability to quench love

EDWIN MORGAN

EN 2584

EN 1985

EN 7211

EN 8749

EN 131

EN 5461

EN 2322

EN 2525

EN 2261

EN 7362

EN 6263

EN 3824

From *Grains of Countryflowers with Lemon, category 4: Feet,* Fritz Schwegler, 1996

Dear...........

Thank you for your letter rejecting my application for employment with your firm.

I have received rejections from an unusually large number of well qualified organisations. With such a varied and promising spectrum of rejections from which to select, it is impossible for me to consider them all. After careful deliberation, then, and because a number of firms have found me more unsuitable, I regret to inform you that I am unable to accept your rejection.

Despite your company's outstanding qualifications and previous experience in rejecting applicants, I find that your rejection does not meet with my requirements at this time. As a result, I will be starting employment with your firm on the first of the month.

Circumstances change and one can never know when new demands for rejection arise. Accordingly I will keep your letter on file in case my requirements for rejection change.

Please do not regard this letter as a criticism of your qualifications in attempting to refuse me employment. I wish you the best of luck in rejecting future candidates.

Sincerely,

John Kador

Duane Hanson, *Executive in Blue Chair*, 1988

North American real estate salesmen celebrating the year's successes by undergoing a mock initiation ceremony. Photograph taken in Manaus, Brazil, by Alex Webb

A Historical and Geographical Event
(in telegram form)

```
GENTLEMEN*:
WOULD YOU LIKE TO JOIN THE GOVERNMENT?
CHARLES DE GAULLE

IN WHAT CAPACITY?
LA CEDILE QUI SOURIT

MINISTERS OF HISTORY AND GEOGRAPHY
CHAREES DE GAULLE

NO THANKS.
LA CEDILLE QUI SOURIT

DONT MENTION IT.
CHARLES DE GAULLE
```

From *Games at the Cedilla, or the Cedilla Takes Off*, George Brecht and Robert Filliou, 1967

THE WORLD BEFORE HIM

" Happiness in our work is obviously of prime importance to us. There can be little surprise in the importance attached today to the right choice of a career."

See page 179

From *Life, The Great Adventure,* The Home Library Club, c.1942

Wim Delvoye, *Cement Mixer*, 1991

Dear Sir,

By the time I arrived at the house where you sent me to make repairs, the storm had torn a good fifty bricks from the roof. So I set up on the roof of the building a beam and a pulley and I hoisted up a couple of baskets of bricks. When I had finished repairing the building there were a lot of bricks left over since I had brought up more than I needed and also because there were some bad, reject bricks that I still had left to bring down. I hoisted the basket back up again and hitched up the line at the bottom. Then I climbed back up again and filled up the basket with the extra bricks. Then I went down to the bottom and untied the line. Unfortunately, the basket of bricks was much heavier than I was and before I knew what was happening, the basket started to plunge down, lifting me suddenly off the ground. I decided to keep my grip and hang on, realizing that to let go would end in disaster – but halfway up I ran into the basket coming down and received a severe blow on the shoulder. I then continued to the top, banging my head against the beam and getting my fingers jammed in the pulley. When the basket hit the ground it burst its bottom, allowing all the bricks to spill out. Since I was now heavier than the basket I started back down again at high speed. Halfway down, I met the basket coming up, and received several severe injuries on my shins. When I hit the ground, I landed on the bricks, getting several more painful cuts and bruises from the sharp edges.

At this moment I must have lost my presence of mind, because I let go of the line. The basket came down again, giving me another heavy blow on the head, and putting me in the hospital. I respectfully request sick leave.

JEAN L'ANSELME, (Found poem)

Hey Ho.... Anonymous photographer, 1958

Sian Bonnell, *Serving suggestion*, 2005

French Agricultural Magazine, 1950

3

THE LIFE OF THE MIND

DeVorss

hamlet / william shakespeare

BANTAM CLASSIC

FC239
50c

What's Eating You?

Keyes / Chivington

HEY, MAN! OPEN UP AND LIVE! Dr. Ken Olson

NON-FICTION

FAWCETT GOLD MEDAL

0-449-14038-5
195

a Katchadourian, *Hamlet* (arranged books from *Composition*), 1993

J.G. BALLARD: THE INDEX

Editor's note. From abundant internal evidence it seems clear that the text printed below is the index to the unpublished and perhaps suppressed autobiography of a man who may well have been one of the most remarkable figures of the 20th century. Yet of his existence nothing is publicly known, although his life and work appear to have exerted a profound influence on the events of the past fifty years. Physician and philosopher, man of action and patron of the arts, sometime claimant to the English throne and founder of a new religion, Henry Rhodes Hamilton was evidently the intimate of the greatest men and women of our age. After World War II he founded a new movement of spiritual regeneration, but private scandal and public concern at his growing megalomania, culminating in his proclamation of himself as a new divinity, seem to have led to his downfall. Incarcerated within an unspecified government institution, he presumably spent his last years writing his autobiography, of which this index is the only surviving fragment.

A substantial mystery still remains. Is it conceivable that all traces of his activities could be erased from our records of the period? Is the suppressed autobiography itself a disguised *roman à clef*, in which the fictional hero exposes the secret identities of his historical contemporaries? And what is the true role of the indexer himself, clearly a close friend of the writer, who first suggested that he embark on his autobiography? This ambiguous and shadowy figure has taken the unusual step of indexing himself into his own index. Perhaps the entire compilation is nothing more than a figment of the over-wrought imagination of some deranged lexicographer. Alternatively, the index may be wholly genuine, and the only glimpse we have into a world hidden from us by a gigantic conspiracy, of which Henry Rhodes Hamilton is the greatest victim.

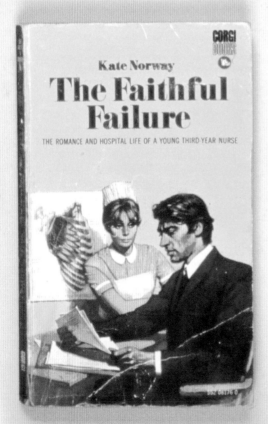

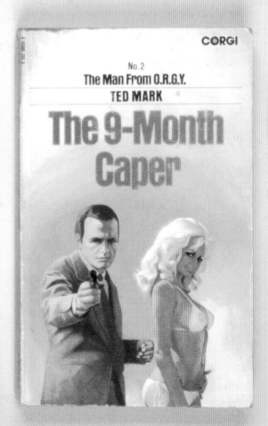

Brighid Lowe, *Love...the tall stranger, the green-eyed monster, the sad-eyed seductress, the faithful failure, the 9-month caper, the boundary line....that's love*, 2006

PAN books G602 2'6

THE
GREEN-EYED MONSTER
Patrick Quentin

A FIRST-CLASS, SUPERBLY CONSTRUCTED, CLASSIC WHODUNIT
Books and Bookmen

PUT IT DOWN IF YOU CAN!
Oxford Mail

J.Oval. 2'6

2/6

carter brown

THE SAD-EYED SEDUCTRESS

One look at her and Danny Boyd knew—a blonde with her kind of eyes . . . would be murder!!!

CORONET

Denise Robins

The Boundary Line

TOPLINER

JOHN L. FOSTER

THAT'S LOVE

TEACH YOURSELF

IGNORANCE

BY

A. EARNSHAW

ENGLISH UNIVERSITIES PRESS LTD.
LONDON

Anthony Earnshaw, *Title Page,* 1974

LEFT: Kada Bux reading a newspaper blindfolded, Studio of Pollard Crowther, 1936

THE INFORMATION MAN

It would be nice if sometime a man would come up to me on the street and say, 'Hello, I'm the Information Man and you have not said the word "yours" for thirteen minutes. You have not said the word "praise" for eighteen days, three hours and nine minutes. You have not used the word "petroleum" in your speech for almost four and a half months, but you wrote the word last Friday evening at 9.35 pm and you used the word "hello" about thirty seconds ago.'

This Information Man would also have details as to the placement and whereabouts of things. He could tell me possibly that of all the books of mine that are out in the public only seventeen are actually placed face up with nothing covering them while 2,026 are under books in vertical positions in libraries and 2,715 are under books in stacks. The most weight upon a single book is 683 pounds and that is in the city of Cologne, Germany, in a bookshop. Fifty-eight have been lost; fourteen totally destroyed by water or fire; while 216 could be considered badly worn. A whopping 319 books are in positions between 40 and 50 degrees and most of these are probably in bookshelves with the stacks leaning at odd angles. Eighteen of the books have never been opened, most of these being newly purchased and put aside momentarily. Of the approximate 5,000 books of Ed Ruscha that have been purchased, only thirty-two have actually been used in a directly functional manner. Thirteen of these have been used as weights for paper or other things. Seven have been used as swatters to kill small insects such as flies and mosquitoes and two have been used in bodily self-defence. Ten have been used to push open heavy doors (probably since they are packaged in tens, one package was used to push open one door). Two were used to nudge wall pictures into correct levels, while one was used as a wiper to check the oil on an auto dipstick. Three are under pillows. Two hundred and twenty-one people have smelled the books' pages, probably most of these on the original purchase.

Three of the books have been in continual motion since their purchase over two years ago, all of these being on a boat near Seattle, Washington...

ED RUSCHA

Aldous Huxley... says that a half-dozen monkeys provided with typewriters would, in a few eternities, produce all the books in the British Museum*. Lewis Carroll observes in the second part of his extraordinary dream novel *Sylvie and Bruno* - in the year 1893 - that as the number of words in any language is limited, so too is the number of their possible combinations or of their books. 'Soon,' he says, 'literary men will not ask themselves, "What book shall I write?" but "Which book?" ' . . .

[Kurd] Lasswitz's basic idea is the same as Carroll's, but the elements of his game are the universal orthographic symbols, not the words of a language. The number of such elements - letters, spaces, brackets, suspension marks, numbers - is reduced and can be reduced even further. The alphabet could relinquish the *q* (which is completely superfluous), the *x* (which is an abbreviation), and all the capital letters. It could eliminate the algorithms in the decimal system of enumeration or reduce them to two, as in Leibniz's binary notation. It could limit punctuation to the comma and the period. There would be no accents, as in Latin. By means of similar simplifications, Lasswitz arrives at twenty-five symbols (twenty-two letters, the space, the period, the comma), whose recombinations and repetitions encompass everything possible to express in all languages. The totality of such variations would form a Total Library of astronomical size. Lasswitz urges mankind to construct that inhuman library, which chance would organise and which would eliminate intelligence...

Everything would be in its blind volumes. Everything: the detailed history of the future, Aeschylus' *The Egyptians*, the exact number of times that the waters of the Ganges have reflected the flight of a falcon, the secret and true name of Rome, the encyclopaedia Novalis would have constructed, my dreams and half-dreams at dawn on August 14, 1934, the proof of Pierre Fermat's theorem, the unwritten chapters of *Edwin Drood*, those same chapters translated into the language spoken by the Garamantes, the paradoxes Berkeley invented concerning Time but didn't publish, Urizen's books of iron, the premature epiphanies of Stephen Dedalus, which would be meaningless before a cycle of a thousand years, the Gnostic Gospel of Basilides, the song the sirens sang, the complete catalogue of the Library, the proof of the inaccuracy of that catalogue. Everything: but for every sensible line or accurate fact there would be millions of meaningless cacophonies, verbal farragoes, and babblings. Everything: but all the generations of mankind could [come to] pass before the dizzying shelves - shelves that obliterate the day and on which chaos lies - ever reward them with a tolerable page.

* Strictly speaking, one immortal monkey would be sufficient.   JORGE LUIS BORGES

HOW I CLASSIFY

My problem with classifications is that they don't last; hardly have I finished putting things into an order before that order is obsolete. Like everyone else, I presume, I am sometimes seized by a mania for arranging things. The sheer number of the things needing to be arranged and the near-impossibility of distributing them according to any truly satisfactory criteria mean that I never finally manage it, that the arrangements I end up with are temporary and vague, and hardly any more effective than the original anarchy.

The outcome of all this leads to truly strange categories. A folder full of miscellaneous papers, for example, on which is written 'To be classified'; or a drawer labelled 'Urgent 1' with nothing in it (in the drawer 'Urgent 2' there are a few old photographs, in 'Urgent 3' some new exercise-books). In short, I muddle along.

BORGES AND THE CHINESE

'(a) belonging to the Emperor, (b) embalmed, (c) domesticated, (d) sucking pigs, (e) sirens, (f) fabulous, (g) dogs running free, (h) included in the present classification, (i) which gesticulate like madmen, (j) innumerable, (k) drawn with a very fine camel-hair brush, (l) etcetera, (m) which have just broken the pitcher, (n) which look from a distance like flies.'

Michel Foucault has hugely popularized this 'classification' of animals which Borges in *Other Inquisitions* attributes to a certain Chinese encyclopedia that one Doctor Franz Kuhn may have held in his hands. The abundance of intermediaries and Borges's well-known love of an ambiguous erudition permit one to wonder whether this rather too perfectly astonishing miscellaneity is not first and foremost an effect of art. An almost equally mind-boggling enumeration might be extracted simply enough from government documents that could hardly be more official:

(a) animals on which bets are laid, (b) animals the hunting of which is banned between 1 April and 15 September, (c) stranded whales, (d) animals whose entry within the national frontiers is subject to quarantine, (e) animals held in joint ownership, (f) stuffed animals, (g) etcetera (this etc is not at all surprising in itself; it's only where it comes in the list that makes it seem odd), (h) animals liable to transmit leprosy, (i) guide-dogs for the blind, (j) animals in receipt of significant legacies, (k) animals able to be transported in the cabin, (l) stray dogs without collars, (m) donkeys, (n) mares assumed to be with foal.

GEORGES PEREC

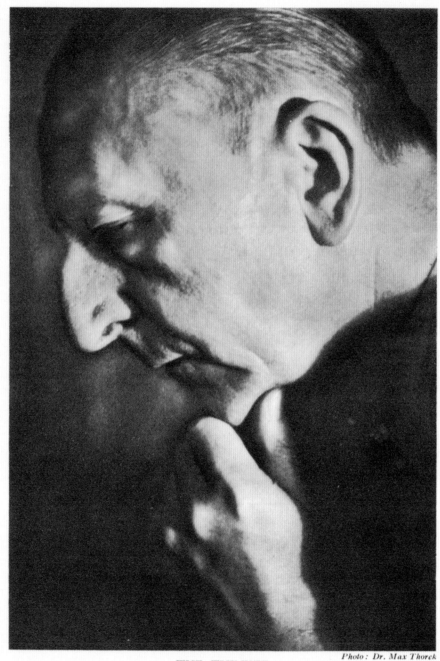

Photo: Dr. Max Thorek

THE THINKER

" Know thyself," says the modern psychologist.   It is through desire, inspired and instructed by imagination that man lays hold upon the world around him, penetrates it, permeates it, draws it back into himself.

See page 79

From *Life: The Great Adventure,* The Home Library Club, c.1942

went into the wood to think something,

but forgot to think and didn't find it

necessary to draw any conclusions from this.

herman de vries, *in the studio*, 1977

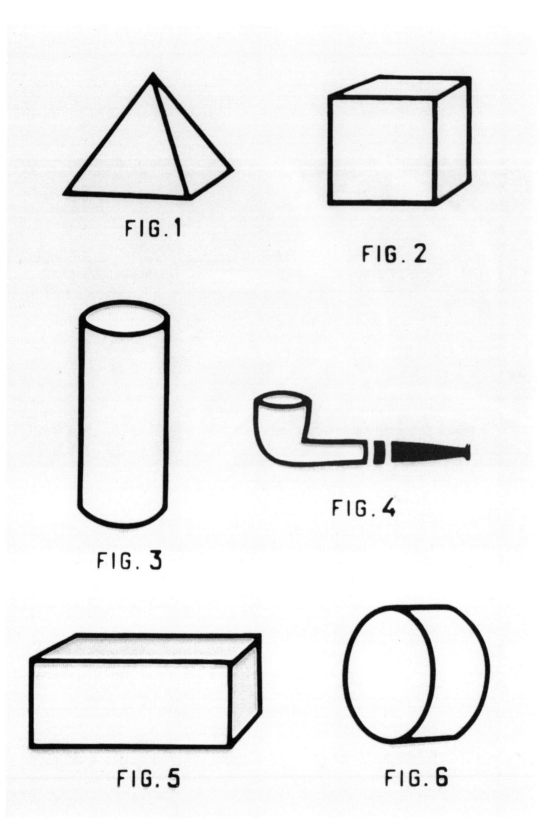

FIG. 1

FIG. 2

FIG. 3

FIG. 4

FIG. 5

FIG. 6

Marcel Broodthaers, *Pipe and Academic Forms*, 1970

Untitled (Racing bicycle and lederhosen), unknown photographer, 1950

FROM THE THIRD POLICEMAN

Did you ever hear of the mollycule theory? Everything do you see is composed of small particles of itself that are flying around in circles, arcs and figures too numerous to mention. Darting backwards and forwards all the time on the go. These gentlemen are called atoms, do you follow me?

Atomics are a very intricate theorem and can be worked out with algebra. Now when you hit a bar of iron with a good coal hammer, the atoms are bashed away by the wallops and some of the atoms of the bar will go into the hammer and vice versa. The gross and net result is that people who spend most of their natural lives riding iron bicycles over the rocky road-steads of this parish get their personalities mixed up with the personalities of the bicycles as a result of the interchanging of the atoms and you would be surprised at the number of people in these parts who are half people and half bicycle. Sometimes even worse. For instance I would reckon the post-man here to be seventy-one per cent bicycle. A round of thirty-eight miles on the bicycle every single day for forty years, hail rain or snow balls, there is very little hope of ever getting his number down below fifty again.

Now a man who is half a bicycle may not look like a bicycle, he would have no back wheel on him and you cannot expect him to grow handlebars. But a man who has let things go too far spends a lot of time leaning on walls or standing propped by one foot at kerbsides.

Of course there are other things to do with ladies and ladies' bicycles that I will mention to you separately at another time. And things I would rather not say too much about. For instance there was a young lady teacher in this district one time that had a new bicycle. She was not very long here when a man who was already half-way to being a bloody bicycle himself went into the lonely countryside on her female bicycle, bouncing over those rocky roads, but worse happened, when the young lady teacher rushed out to go somewhere in a hurry, her bicycle was gone but here was your young man's leaning there very conveniently and trying to look very small and comfortable and attractive. Need I tell you what the result was, or what happened. Your man had a day out with the lady's bicycle and her with the man's bicycle. And it's quite clear that the lady in the case had a high number, thirty-five or forty per cent I would say. Can you appreciate the immorality of that?

FLANN O'BRIEN

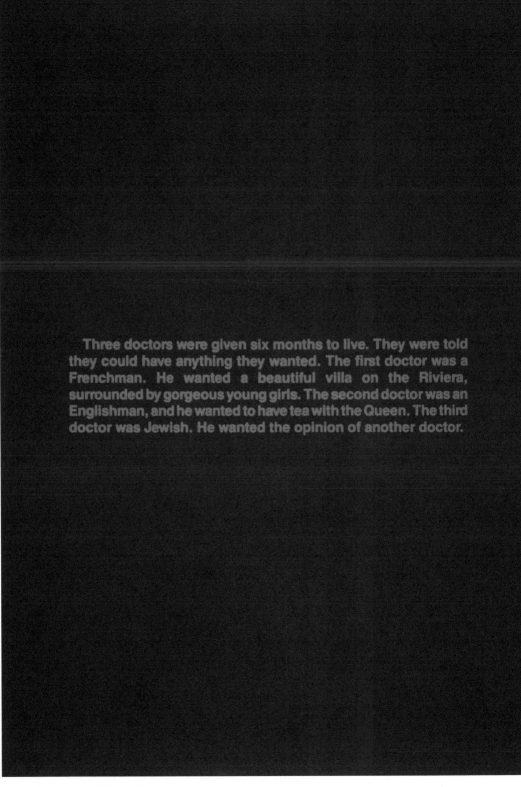

Three doctors were given six months to live. They were told they could have anything they wanted. The first doctor was a Frenchman. He wanted a beautiful villa on the Riviera, surrounded by gorgeous young girls. The second doctor was an Englishman, and he wanted to have tea with the Queen. The third doctor was Jewish. He wanted the opinion of another doctor.

Richard Prince, *Untitled,* 1990

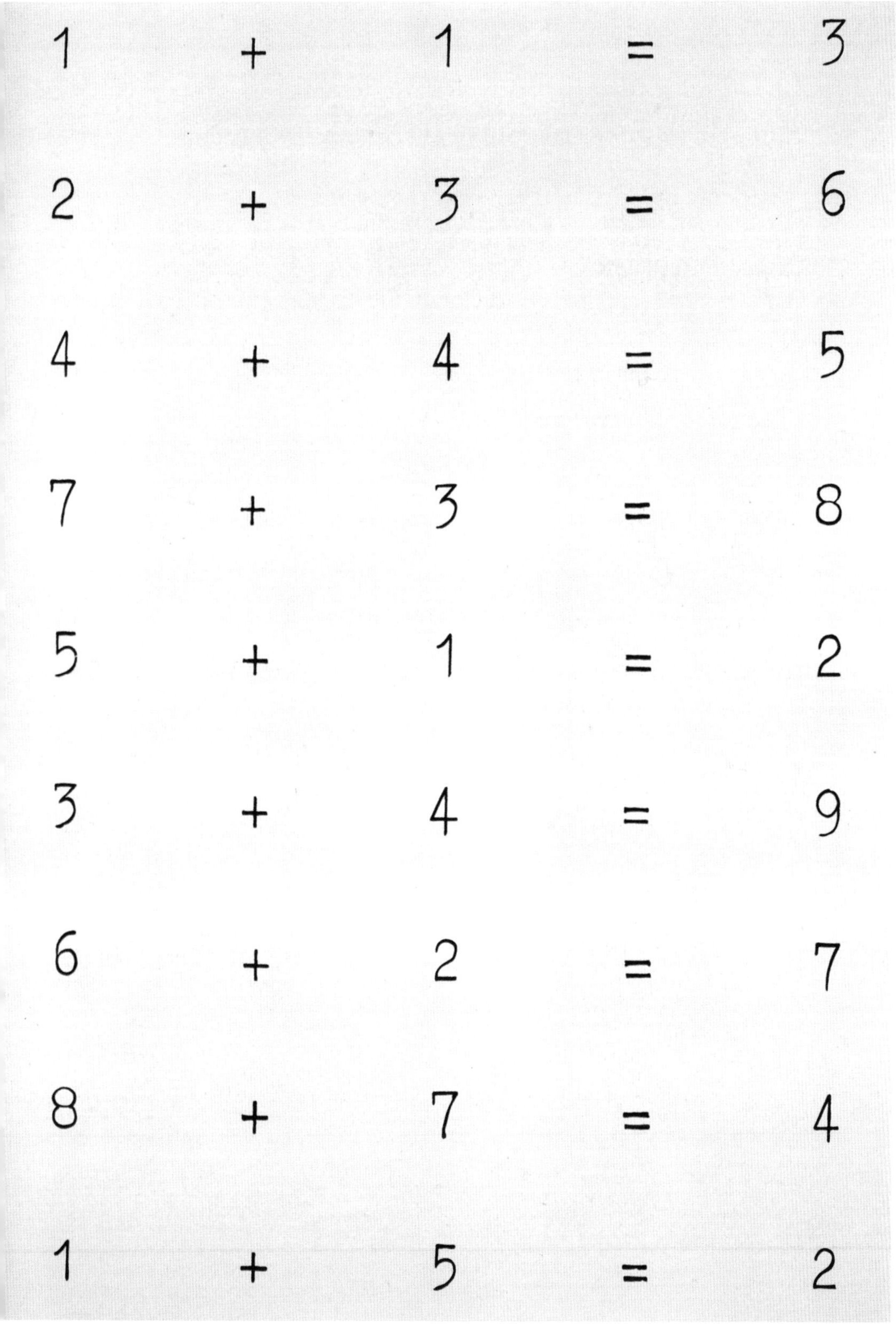

$1 + 1 = 3$

$2 + 3 = 6$

$4 + 4 = 5$

$7 + 3 = 8$

$5 + 1 = 2$

$3 + 4 = 9$

$6 + 2 = 7$

$8 + 7 = 4$

$1 + 5 = 2$

Sigmar Polke, *Solutions V*, 1967

THE RED-HAIRED MAN

There was a red-haired man who had no eyes or ears. Neither did he have any hair, so he was called red-haired theoretically.

He couldn't speak, since he didn't have a mouth. Neither did he have a nose. He didn't even have any arms or legs. He had no stomach and he had no back and he had no spine and he had no innards whatsoever. He had nothing at all! Therefore there's no knowing whom we are even talking about.

In fact it's better we don't say any more about him.

DANIIL KHARMS

4

MISCELLANEOUS

on't be afraid to use oddities

is queer item is a piece of dried seaweed. It needs only a base to become a
versation piece. Because its form is so involved it would be most effective
inst a bare or very simple background.

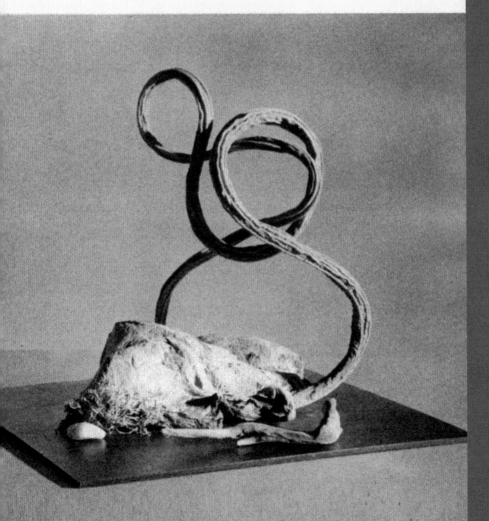

From *The Art of Driftwood and Dried Arrangements,* by Tatsuo Ishimoto, 1951

ART AND CRAFT

Shi Xinning, *Duchamp's Retrospective Exhibition in China*, 2000-2001

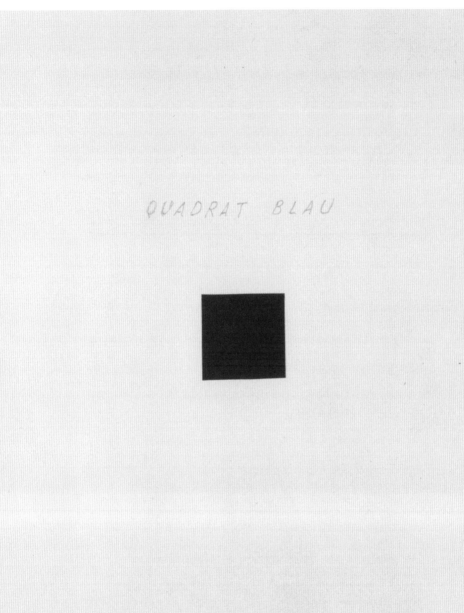

Joan Brossa, *Blue Square,* 1970

HUMPHREY: No, Laura, I don't think it's the kind of thing we could expect Graham to show much interest in.

LAURA: Oh?

HUMPHREY: He's very orthodox in many ways. As far as his painting is concerned.

LAURA: I must say he doesn't show much preference for orthodox methods in anything else.

HUMPHREY: All the same, Laura, I think that to fit the brush in a vice and move the canvas about on the end of it would create more problems than it would solve.

LAURA: I should have thought it would have been the very thing for Graham.

HUMPHREY: I'll suggest it to him, of course - but you mustn't be surprised if he turns it down. Don't forget he's got all this fuss on his mind still about Colonel Padlock's portrait - that must be taking up practically every spare minute of his time.

LAURA: What fuss about Colonel Padlock's portrait? He's finished it. He *must* have.

HUMPHREY: It isn't just a matter of setting an easel up, Laura, and a canvas, and beginning to paint. Just like that.

LAURA: I think that's absolutely disgraceful! What for heaven's sake has he been doing?

HUMPHREY: He hasn't been wasting his time, my dear.

LAURA: Six weeks it must be since all this started. At least. I can't think what he can have been doing all that time.

HUMPHREY: So far as I know, Colonel Padlock hasn't complained.

LAURA: Why on earth doesn't he get people to help him?

HUMPHREY: You won't persuade Graham to delegate responsibility, my dear.

LAURA: Doing every single thing himself from scratch.

HUMPHREY: Yes, well, there it is. If he prefers to work that way . . .

LAURA: I'd say nothing if it were simply a question of constructing his own easels. With home-made glue.

HUMPHREY: After all . . .

LAURA: Or even weaving his canvases himself. But growing his own hemp or whatever it is to do it with! That's carrying it too far.

HUMPHREY: Yes, well - I'm afraid I side with Graham over this, Laura.

LAURA: Felling the timber himself for his brush handles and planing it down till it's small enough.

HUMPHREY: What other way is there, Laura, if you're determined to keep control over the finished picture? And that's the whole crux of it as far as Graham is concerned. As you know.

LAURA: And in the meantime, Colonel Padlock has to sit there.

HUMPHREY: As far as that goes, I should think Colonel Padlock would be the last person to want to see Graham compromise his professional integrity on his account.

LAURA: So he just has to sit waiting. While Graham goes off all over the world looking for natural pigments and one thing and another.

HUMPHREY: My dear Laura, what else can he possibly do but collect the pigments? He can't paint without them. Be sensible.

LAURA: No. *(Quietly and unemphatically after a brief pause.)* But there's an artist's colourman not three doors away.

HUMPHREY: You don't seem to understand, Laura.

LAURA: And I can't see how it could possibly hurt his professional integrity to at least buy his brushes ready-made.

HUMPHREY: Perhaps not, but . . .

LAURA: A whole Sunday morning spent going over one camel for the sake of three or four miserable hairs! It's utterly ridiculous!

HUMPHREY: In any case, that part of it's more or less finished. It's this wretched problem now of where to sit Colonel Padlock. How far back from the easel.

LAURA: *(After a shocked pause.)* That was decided.

HUMPHREY: Not finally, my dear.

LAURA: It really is too bad!

HUMPHREY: Yes, well . . .

LAURA: How many months is it since we all sat round listening to Graham explaining about "giving the background a chance" and "not letting the sitter choke the canvas" and all the rest of it?

HUMPHREY: It's one thing to have worked something out in principle, Laura. It's a different matter putting it into practice.

LAURA: All he has to do surely is to sit Colonel Padlock far enough back from the easel. That shouldn't take him eight weeks.

HUMPHREY: Don't forget Colonel Padlock is travelling backwards. It's bound to slow him down a little bit.

LAURA: *Travelling* backwards?

HUMPHREY: You know Graham as well as I do, my dear. He doesn't often do things by halves.

Pause.

LAURA: That, I suppose, accounts for his sending home for field-glasses.

HUMPHREY: It's gone well beyond field-glasses, Laura.

LAURA: Oh? What is it now, then? Descriptions once a week by transatlantic telephone?

HUMPHREY: Every half hour, actually. By ticker tape.

LAURA: *(Weakly.)* I see.

HUMPHREY: Or that was the position at any rate last week. He was in Yokohama then.

LAURA: Who was in Yokohama?

HUMPHREY: Colonel Padlock. *(Pause.)* He's in all probability more than half-way round the globe by now.

LAURA: Oh. *(Pause.)* What happens when he's circled it?

HUMPHREY: They're expecting to end up back to back.

LAURA: Back to what?

HUMPHREY: That's if Graham's calculations are as reliable as he thinks they are.

Pause.

LAURA: I see.

HUMPHREY: And by that time he hopes to have the television cameras ready. *(Pause.)* Rigged up behind him. *(Pause.)* And if he puts the screen where he can get a clear view of it while he's painting, he can go right ahead the moment Colonel Padlock comes in range of the cameras. *(Pause.)* I think it rather appeals to Graham - the idea of painting direct from a television screen. *(Pause.)* It would, of course.

Long pause.

LAURA: I suppose as soon as he gets back we ought to send him a greetings telegram.

HUMPHREY: Who?

LAURA: Colonel Padlock. If he ever does.

Pause.

HUMPHREY: I suppose we ought.

CURTAIN

Pavel Büchler, *The Critic,* 2001

Definitely built for the man who likes to be carefree about his clothes—that's the nice way of putting "for the lazy man." And this is the ideal labour-saving garment—zipp fastener, turn-down collar, and it goes over anything.

Lord Berners at work, unknown photographer, c.1940

THE CURATOR TORE PAST THE
MALEVICH AT BREAKNECK SPEED

Glen Baxter, 2004

Höhere Wesen befahlen: rechte obere Ecke schwarz
malen!

Sigmar Polke, *The Higher Powers Command: Paint the Right Hand Corner Black!*, 1969

JOSEPH ROTH: ARCHITECTURE

It happens from time to time that I fail to distinguish a cabaret from a crematorium, and pass certain scenes actually intended to be amusing, with the quiet shudder that the attributes of death still elicit. Such confusions would not have been possible in previous years. Ugliness, coarseness, and failure could always be brought into some relation to beauty, elegance and good quality. A building that bore a fleeting, if distressing, resemblance to a classical temple was certain to be a theatre for light opera. Something resembling a church was a main railway station. It was embarrassing, but somehow handy. You knew exactly how the deception operated, and never failed to recognize the fake when you saw the true. If you thought you saw marble, you knew you were in the presence of plasterboard. But ever since people have had the idea that modern times needed 'modern styles,' all the old rules of thumb have stopped helping me. It's as if all the gobbledygook I've learned with so much effort has suddenly been invalidated. It happens from time to time that in my hurry to catch a train I look for a cinema, thinking thereby to find the station. But my method no longer works. The building I took for the station turns out to be a 'five o'clock tea' house in a sports palace. The facades of these modern times are unsettling me.

Still more confusing is interior design. I have learned that those hygienic white operating theatres are actually patisseries. But I continue to mistake those long glass tubes mounted on walls for thermometers. Of course, they are lamps, or as people more correctly say, 'sources of illumination.' A glass tabletop isn't really there to permit the diner to view his own boots in comfort during a meal, but to help a metal ashtray produce those marrow-piercing, grating sounds when slid across it. There is a class of objects that are wide, white, hard-wearing, deep, and hollow; have no feet; and look like chests. On these, it seems, people sit. Of course they aren't anything as straightforward as chairs, but rather 'seating accommodation.' Similar confusions are also possible with those living objects collectively referred to as 'staff.' A girl in red pants and blue jacket with gold buttons, with a round fez on her head, whom – but for the fact that the treachery of these times has begun to dawn on me – I would certainly have taken for a man, but then was foolish enough to take for a sort of royal guard in a costume drama. In fact this girl is in charge of the cloakroom, and of the sales of cigarettes and of those long, slender unjointed silk dolls, who look like merry hanged corpses.

Domestic interior design is a fraught affair. It makes me hanker for the mild and soothing and tasteless red velvet interiors in which people lived so undiscriminatingly no more than twenty years ago. It was unhygienic, dark, cool, probably stuffed full of dangerous bacteria, and pleasant. The accumulation of small, useless, fragile, cheap, but tenderly bred knick-knacks on sideboards and mantelpieces produced an agreeable contempt that made one feel at home right away. Countering all the tormenting demands of health, windows were kept closed, no noise came up from the street to interrupt the useless and sentimental family conversations. Soft carpets, harbouring innumerable dangerous diseases, made life seem livable and even sickness bearable, and in the evenings the vulgar chandeliers spread a gentle, cheerful light that was like a form of happiness.

The lives of our fathers' generation were lived in such poor taste. But their children and grandchildren live in strenuously bracing conditions. Not even nature itself affords as much light and air as some of the new dwellings. For a bedroom there is a glass-walled studio. They dine in gyms. Rooms you would have sworn were tennis courts serve them as libraries and music rooms. Water whooshes in thousands of pipes. They do Swedish exercises in vast aquariums. They relax after meals on white operating tables. And in the evening concealed fluorescent tubes light the room so evenly that it is no longer illuminated, it is a pool of luminosity.

Bee beard, unknown photographer, c.1950

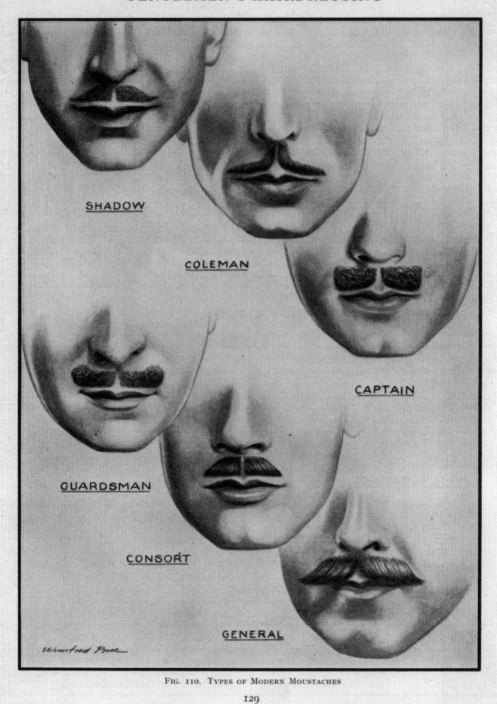

FIG. 110. TYPES OF MODERN MOUSTACHES

129

10—(B.6144)

From *The Art and Craft of Hairdressing,* Gilbert A. Foan, c. 1935

TO THE ONE UPSTAIRS

Boss of all bosses of the universe.
Mr know-it-all, wheeler-dealer, wire-puller,
And whatever else you're good at.
Go ahead, shuffle your zeros tonight.
Dip in ink the comets' tails.
Staple the night with starlight.

You'd be better off reading coffee dregs,
Thumbing the pages of the Farmer's Almanac.
But no! You love to put on airs,
And cultivate your famous serenity
While you sit behind your big desk
With zilch in your in-tray, zilch
In your out-tray,
And all of eternity spread around you.

Doesn't it give you the creeps
To hear them begging you on their knees,
Sputtering endearments,
As if you were an inflatable, life-size doll?
Tell them to button up and go to bed.
Stop pretending you're too busy to take notice.

Your hands are empty and so are your eyes.
There's nothing to put your signature to,
Even if you knew your own name,
Or believed the ones I keep inventing,
As I scribble this note to you in the dark.

CHARLES SIMIC

EVENINGS AT 7
IN THE PARISH HALL

MON	ALCOHOLICS ANONYMOUS
TUE	ABUSED SPOUSES
WED	EATING DISORDERS
THU	SAY NO TO DRUGS
FRI	TEEN SUICIDE WATCH
SAT	SOUP KITCHEN

SUNDAY SERMON
8 A.M.

"AMERICA'S JOYOUS
FUTURE"

Erika Rothenberg, *America's Joyous Future*, 1990

Ed Ruscha, *She Sure Knew Her Devotionals*, 1976

Peter Paul Atzwanger, *Untitled, (Gift of God)*, Germany, c.1930

THE OYSTER

The oyster is about as large as a medium-sized pebble, but rougher looking and less uniform in colour, brilliantly whitish. An obstinately closed world, which, however, can be opened: grasp it in the hollow of a dishcloth, use a chipped, not too sharp knife, then give it a few tries. Prying fingers cut themselves on it, and break their nails: crude work. Blows mark its envelope with white circles, sorts of halos.

Inside, a whole world, both food and drink: under a *firmament* (strictly speaking) of mother-of-pearl, the heavens above sinking onto the heavens below form a mere puddle, a viscous, greenish sack fringed with blackish lace that ebbs and flows in your eyes and nostrils.

Sometimes, though rarely, a formula purls from its nacreous throat, which is immediately used as a personal adornment.

FRANCIS PONGE

Immortal Trout

Stuff some trout with chopped nuts and fry them in olive oil.
Then wrap the trout in very thin slices of calves' liver.

The Excited Pig

A whole salami, skinned, is served upright on a dish containing
some very hot black coffee mixed with a good deal of eau de Cologne.

Devil in Black Key

2/4 orange juice
1/4 grappa
1/4 liquid chocolate
Put in a hard-boiled egg

Futurist menu and recipes by the Aeropainter Fillia , 1932

tablets 8mg

Each tablet contains
8mg ondansetron
as ondansetron hydrochloride dihydrate
Also contains lactose and maize starch

10 tablets

HirstDamien

Damien Hirst, *The Last Supper\Omelette*, 1999

ABSINTHE MAKES THE HEART GROW WARMER

WAITER, what was in that glass?

Arsenic, Sir.

Arsenic. I asked you to ring me absinthe.

I thought you said arsenic. I beg your pardon, Sir.

Do you realise what you've done, you clumsy fool? I'm dying.

I am extremely sorry, Sir.

I DISTINCTLY SAID ABSINTHE.

I realise that I owe you an apology, Sir. I am extremely sorry.

Flann O'Brien, from *The Best of Myles*, 1968

Sian Bonnell, *Serving suggestions*, 2003 & 2005

from *The Cedilla Cookbook*

One new dish and one new dessert for our friend Daniel "le Chef" Spoerri.

Main dish:

6 pounds of turnips
1 clove
9 gallons of water

Put the water on to boil.
Push the clove into one of the turnips.
Throw the 6 pounds of turnips into the boiling water.

Dessert:

an apple pie
an olive

Push the olive into the apple pie

Serves:

Daniel, Kichka and 15 Greek guests on the island of Simi.

From *Games at the Cedilla, or the Cedilla Takes Off,* Robert Filliou and George Brecht, 1967

VARIATIONS ON A THEME

Feeling much worse

Feeling about the same

Feeling particularly better

Feeling a lot better

Feeling a little worse

Feeling worse, then much better

Feeling much better quite quickly

Feeling worse, then much better,

    then worse again

Feeling about the same

J. Brostoff & L. Gamlin, *Food Allergy and Intolerance*, 1989
From *Collected Poems* by Pavel Büchler, 2001

Doing the daily dozen. The active man needs underclothes that will fit and that will give him freedom of movement. This vest and pants set was designed along these lines. It is economical in material too, for it is knitted in 2-ply. The pants are fitted trimly into the waist and are finished with elastic braid.

From *Knitting For All*, 1947

Christ

St. Philip   St. John   St. Thomas   St. Andrew

St. Bartholomew

St. Matthew   St. Simon

St. Thaddeus

St. James the Less   St. James the Greater

St. Peter

Judas

Simon Patterson, *The Last Supper Arranged According to the Flat Back Four Formation
(Jesus Christ in Goal)*, 1990

David Shrigley, *Red Card,* 1996

Richard Brown

INDOOR GOLF

A. G. HAVERS (COOMBE HILL GOLF CLUB) SWINGING—THE
"FOLLOW THROUGH"

From *The Brain and Golf, Some Hints for Golfers from Modern Mental Science* , C. W. Bailey, 1923

SWINGING.

From *Women's Health* manual, c.1932

PIERRE BETTENCOURT: SINKING CONTEST

In La Mancha province, I possess seven and a half acres of quicksands on which I organise sinking contests. The prizes in the lottery, totalling about a million, are not to be sniffed at. From the first issue of tickets, competitors rushed to take part.

'The rules are very simple', I tell them, 'the last to disappear wins.'

They stepped forward and were each in turn sucked up by the sands. Those who struggled sank more quickly than the others. Most of them, suddenly scared out of their wits and bitterly regretting their rash involvement in this venture, yelled for me to come and extricate them. One by one, their heads disappeared. A few arms still stuck out from the surface. Then nothing. Only a big, strapping fellow from Roussillon, just across the border, was more or less holding his own at shoulder level, a broad smile on his face: 'I think I've won,' he called out to me rather breathlessly.

From the cement strip on which I was standing I had only to throw him the rope. But I calculated rapidly that my million would come in very useful in subsidising the invention of fresh enterprises, and that after all I was the only witness of this lad who had already sunk so deep that he could no longer turn his head to verify the fact that the surface around him was empty. From where I was standing I made violent signals to him as if to explain that there was still another competitor left, right behind him.

I shall never forget the look of hatred that he shot me before disappearing.

Robert Filliou, *Un, Eins, One....* (detail), 1984

ITEM 107. (LA 25+) *Engages in beneficial recreation.*

This item may seem to be irrelevant in the occupational category. It represents a continuation of those early self-initiated personal activities which reflect social maturation without necessarily productive outcome. But even if these engagements do yield practical returns, our interest centers not so much on these fruits as on the otherwise profitable use of leisure time.

The item is to be interpreted as seriously purposive adult recreation as contrasted with mere sitting around or relaxing in passive amusement as spectator or listener rather than as an active participant. In other words, the activities reflect a mature display of need for development of what might be called personal self-expression outside the field of economic necessity. These absorptions are extremely varied in such fields as athletics, literature, music, art, drama, gardening, collecting, travel, serious discussion of important topics, and in general the more advantageous forms of worthwhile diversions. Some of the more specifically socially directed forms of correlated activities will be found in the superior level of the socialization category.

Like most of the superior adult items, this item is difficult to define because of its varied forms of expression and because of the difficulty of placing a proper value on the level of development which the activities reflect. The examiner is therefore cautioned against scoring the item too generously. The performances involved are basically related to making profitable use of leisure time for safeguarding or improving the S's mental and physical welfare. This is witnessed in serious reading, healthful games and sports, constructive hobbies, creative gardening or breeding, musical performance and appreciation, serious dramatic and artistic interests, and so on. Merely passive interests, casual amusement, or pre-adult pastimes are not to be credited at this level. The examiner must distinguish between youthful and adult recreations of the same order but different purpose and outcome, and this calls for discreet judgment as well as sophisticated discrimination.

From *The Measurement of Social Competence: A manual for the Vineland Social Maturity Scale*, 1953

JOHN SLADEK: ANXIETAL REGISTER (B)

DIRECTIONS.

READ CAREFULLY. Before answering any of the questions below, be sure to have all pages of this form, in order.

Fill out in triplicate, using ballpoint pen or, preferably, indelible pencil. Press hard. PLEASE PRINT. Sign name to all copies.

1. State full name at present: _____

2. Full name at birth, or baptism: _____

3. Give any aliases, abbreviations, or nicknames by which you have ever been known:

   _____

4. Attach copies of birth and baptismal certificates.

5. Social security number: _____

6. Name on your last income tax return: _____

7. Date: _____

8. Date of tax return: _____

9. State your full permanent address: _____

   _____

10. Where may you be quickly reached by:

    a) Mail: _____

    b) Telephone: _____

    c) Telegram or cable: _____

    d) Messenger: _____

11. List every address at which you have resided, since birth, in chronological order. Include every address, with the

    following exceptions:

    a) Hotel accommodations in the United States, Mexico or Canada,

    for stays of up to or less than three days, occurring more than five years ago.

    b) Accommodations at U.S. Embassies, in other than an official capacity,

    for any duration, occurring more than seventeen years ago.

    c) Antarctic expeditions not using APO addresses.

    ALL OTHER ADDRESSES MUST BE SHOWN, WITHOUT EXCEPTION.

    Note: extra sheets (Form AR-B Supplem.) may be attached.

Street address:	City:	State:	Date from:	Date to:

12. Occupation: _____

13. Name and address of company where you are presently employed/were last employed:

    _____

    a) Last position held: _____

14. Salary: _____

15. Name of superior: _____

16. Starting date: _____

17. Terminating date: _____

18. Attach references.

19. If unemployed, give reason: _____

20. Why did you leave your last job? _____

21. Give your entire employment history, except for your last or present job. List all employment in chronological order,

    and include part-time employment. Note: Extra sheets (Form AR-B Supplem.) may be attached.

Company name & address:	Position supervisor:	Salary from: To:

Reason for leaving: _____

22. Have you ever been fired for: _____

    a) Theft: _____

    b) Embezzlement: _____

    c) Dishonesty: _____

    d) False references: _____

    e) Absenteeism: _____

    f) Tardiness: _____

    g) Loafing: _____

    h) Inefficiency: _____

    i) Personal reasons: Explain: _____

23. Have you ever quarrelled with fellow employees? _____

24. Have you ever had difficulty with employers? Describe: _____

25. Have you ever stolen any property belonging to an employer, no matter how small in value? _____

26. Have you ever feigned illness? _____

27. Name of your bank or banks? _____

28. Explain any foreign bank accounts: _____

29. Bank Account Number(s): _____

30. Present balance(s): _____

31. Number and amount of withdrawals during past year: _____

32. Father's name: _____

33. Mother's maiden name: _____

34. Attach birth certificate and marriage licence.

35. Have you ever been arrested

    a) As a minor: _____

    b) As an adult: _____

    c) Misdemeanor? _____

    d) Felony? _____

    e) Convicted? _____

    f) Sentenced? _____

36. Give full details of any arrest and/or conviction, including name of offence, whether convicted, sentence and/or fine. Include all traffic offences other than overtime parking.

37. Do you love your mother more than your father? _____

38. If you do not love your mother, explain: _____

39. Circle which of the following you have ever suffered from: a) Rheumatism b) Arthritis c) Chronic fatigue d) Rupture e) Tuberculosis f) Night sweats g) Nocturnal emissions h) Nightmares (frequent) i) Sleepwalking j) Ringing noises k) Chronic or severe headaches l) Bronchitis m) Homosexual tendencies n) Hot flushes o) Tumours p) Cancer q) Gastric ulcer r) Gonorrhea s) Syphilis t) Asthma u) Hay fever v) Severe cough w) Trenchmouth x) Hepatitis (jaundice) y) Diabetes z) Anaemia aa) Poliomyelitis ab) Heart attack ac) Stroke ad) Heart murmur ae) Blindness af) Deafness ag) Tunnel vision ah) Astigmatism ai) Unexplainable pains (Explain) aj) Visions ak) Epilepsy al) Impotence am) Obesity an) Chronic nausea ao) Drug addiction (Explain) ap) Alcoholism aq) Double vision ar) Frequent or severe accidents as) Amnesia at) Laryngitis au) Malnutrition av) Precognition aw) Cleft palate ax) Harelip ay) Multiple digits az) Paralysis (specify).

40. Have you ever had any serious physical or mental disorder?
Describe, specifying dates, physician, treatment, hospitalization etc.: _____

41. Briefly describe your own condition at present: _____

42. Are you under medication? Describe: _____

43. Attach medical records and physician's affidavit. _____

44. Have you ever undergone surgery? Describe: _____

45. Have you all your natural teeth? Attach chart: _____

46. Describe any amputations, giving dates and reasons: _____

47. Have you:

a) Both kidneys b) Both lungs c) Ovaries d) Prostate e) Gall bladder f) Both eyes g) A bladder

h) A complete stomach i) A complete colon j) Both breasts k) Lower jaw l) Nose

48. Have you ever undergone sterilization?

49. Castration? _____

50. Hysterectomy? _____

51. Do you feel sexual desire for, about, during:

a) Those of your own sex b) Those of both sexes c) Children d) Your mother e) Your father f) Your son

g) Your daughter h) Sister i) Brother j) Babies k) Cadavers l) Animals m) Birds n) Fish o) Insects p) Cripples

q) People who hurt you r) People whom you hurt s) People of special professions (describe) t) People in particular

costumes (describe) u) Watching others in the act of coition v) Peeping at naked persons w) Drinking blood

x) Drinking urine y) Drinking semen z) Eating faeces aa) Looking at photographs ab) Looking at drawings

ac) Drawing pictures ad) Telephoning ae) Confessing sins af) Listening to music ag) Dancing ah) Exposing one's sex organs

to someone else ai) Anal entry aj) Axilial entry ak) Oral entry al) Nasal entry am) Rape an) All members of the opposite

sex, regardless of age or condition ao) Watching movies ap) Watching television aq) Performing your ordinary work

ar) Masturbating as) Urinating at) Defecating au) Menstruating av) Wearing clothing belonging to the opposite sex

aw) A particular part of another's body ax) Of your body ay) Crowds az) Rubbing against people ba) Clergy

bb) Weapons bc) Machines bd) Plants be) Trees bf) Sunsets bg) People of other races bh) Apparel bi) Dangerous

or unusual surroundings bj) Inanimate objects bk) Mathematical propositions bl) Thoughts bm) The law bn) God

bo) The act of filling out a form.

52. List all the persons in your household:

Person: _____ Age: _____ Sex: _____

Income: _____ Source: _____ Relation to you: _____

53. Why do you believe you have been asked to fill out this form? _____

_____

54. Describe briefly your feelings about filling out this form: _____

55. Describe in detail other forms you have been asked to fill out, explain their use, and estimate your performance:

_____

_____

56. Describe your character in detail, giving examples of your behaviour to illustrate points.

Note: extra sheets (Form AR-B Supplem) may be attached.

_____

_____

_____

57. Do you believe in God? _____ If 'no', explain: _____

58. Have you answered all the above questions? _____

59. Have you answered truthfully? _____

60. Have you ever lied? _____

61. Have you ever stolen anything? _____

62. Why do you believe that you have been asked to fill out this form? _____

_____

_____

_____

63. If you are merely reading this form, why do you believe that you have not been asked to fill it out?

_____

64. Have you been asked to fill out this form? _____

65. To read it? _____

66. Not to fill it out? _____

67. Not to read it? Explain: _____

68. Compare this form with others which you may have read or filled out, whether or not you were asked to read them
    or fill them out: _____

69. Be sure your comparison is fair and correct. If it is not, you may rewrite it on extra sheets (Form AR-B Supplem).
    If you do so, be sure your revision is correct.

70. Was your original comparison correct? _____ Fair? If not, explain:
    _____
    _____
    _____

71. If you revised your comparison, why?
    _____

72. Write your life history in brief, explaining in passing your answers to questions 11, 21, 39 and 51 fully. Take as much
    time, and as many extra sheets (Form AR-B Supplem.) as necessary, but do not lie, omit, falsify, distort or invent.
    If there are any portions you genuinely do not fully remember, you will be asked to complete and attach three copies
    of Form WH6, Hypnotic Drugs Waiver of Rights.
    _____
    _____
    _____
    _____
    _____

73. Sign the following statement:
    I hereby agree to submit to a Keeler Polygraph ("Lie Detector") examination, to be conducted by or in the presence of a
    psychiatrist and police officer, during which I will endeavour to answer all or any questions about my past life as truthfully as
    I am able.
    (X) Signed: _____
    Witnessed: _____

74. Describe your feelings upon reading and signing the above statement:
    _____
    _____

75. Do you believe you have anything to hide, about your past life? If not, explain:
    _____
    _____
    _____

76. Have you anything to add, regarding the answers to questions 11, 21, 33, 39, 51, 72 or 75?
    _____
    _____
    _____

77. Do you ever have feelings of anxiety? _____
    I swear that all the statements above are true and complete and that I have not attempted any falsification,
    on penalty of perjury.
    (X) Signed: _____
    Witnessed: _____

Low Self-Esteem Support Group will meet Thursday at

7.00-8.30 pm. Please use the back door.

Notice posted on church bulletin board.

THE ARTIST AND THE CLOCK

Serov, an artist, went to the Obvodniy Canal. Why did he go there? To buy some india rubber. What did he want india rubber for? To make himself a rubber band. And what did he want a rubber band for? In order to stretch it. That's what for. And what else? This is what else: the artist Serov had broken his clock. The clock had been going well, but he picked it up and broke it. What else? Nothing else. Nothing, this is it, in a nutshell! Keep your filthy snout out when it's not needed! And may the Lord have mercy on us!

Once there lived an old woman. She lived and loved, until she got burnt up in her stove. Served her right, too! The artist Serov, at least, was of that opinion . . .

Huh! I would write some more, but the ink-pot has suddenly gone and disappeared.

DANIIL KHARMS

Joan Brossa, *The Egg of Chaos,* 1988

THE CLOCK

In the tenth century
a monk named Gilbert
put together the first
mechanical clock:
the human spirit's yearning
towards the Eternal Infinite
needed to be marked off
by a regular sound.
It needed a balance wheel,
an acrobat hanging on a bar
coming loose.

The regular sound begot bells
the synchronized bells
begot towns,
the towns begot cities, the cities begot more hours,
the hours begot
minutes,
the minutes begot
seconds,
a second begot a moment.

And there is no nature in a moment.
No town. No bells, no tick.
No monk. No ash.

The acrobat in the cupola
reaches for a bar
which isn't there.

MIROSLAV HOLUB

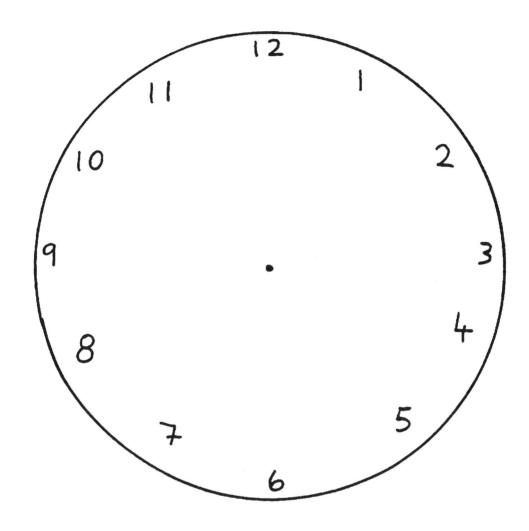

Q. WHAT TIME IS IT ?

A. I DON'T KNOW

David Shrigley, *What Time is it?* 2004

NOTES ON CONTRIBUTORS

Peter Paul Atzwanger, Austria, 1888-1974: sculptor and photographer

J.G. Ballard, UK, b.1930: 'New Wave' science fiction writer and novelist

Glen Baxter. UK, b.1944: artist, surrealist

Pierre Bettencourt, France, 1917-2006: poet, writer, Art Brut painter, avant-garde publisher

Sian Bonnell, UK, b.1956: artist-photographer of the unlikely

Jorge Luis Borges, Argentina, 1899-1986: writer, fabulist, poet, librarian

Marcel Broodthaers, Belgium, 1924-1976: surrealistic and poetic artist, filmmaker and writer

Joan Brossa, Spain, 1919-1998: surrealist artist, poet, playwright and designer

Pavel Büchler, Czechoslovakia, b.1952: subversive artist, writer and teacher

Jacques Carelman, France, b.1929: painter, theatre designer and writer

Les Coleman, UK, b.1945: artist, cartoonist, writer and wit

Adam Dant, UK, b.1967: artist, writer, map-maker, creator of Donald Parsnips

Anthony Earnshaw, UK, 1924-2004: anarchist, surrealist artist, aphorist and illustrator

Robert Filliou, France, 1926-1989: Fluxus artist working in film, sculpture, and performance

Douglas Gordon, UK, b.1966: installation artist, filmmaker and moralist

Duane Hanson, USA, 1925-1996: hyper-realist sculptor of the mundane

Werner Hauser, Switzerland, artist and photographer

Damien Hirst, UK, b.1965: prolific artist of mortality, working in many media

Miroslav Holub, Czechoslovakia, 1923-1998: poet and immunologist

John Kador, Hungary (USA since 1956), b.1950: independent business author

Franz Kafka, Bohemia, 1883-1924: darkly absurdist novelist and short story writer

Wassily Kandinsky, Russia, 1866-1944: abstract painter and art theoretician

Nina Katchadourian, USA, b.1968: photographer, video artist and sculptor

Daniil Kharms, Russia, 1905-1942: early Soviet-era absurdist and satirical writer

Andrey Kurkov, Ukraine, b.1961: absurdist and satirical writer

Brighid Lowe, UK, b.1965: witty artist and text maker

Edwin Morgan, Scotland, b.1920: poet in diverse styles, translator

Simon Patterson, UK, b.1967: artist and logician

Georges Perec, France, 1936-1982: Oulipian novelist, writer, essayist and wit

Fernando Pessoa, Portugal, 1888-1935: poet in diverse styles, melancholic

Sigmar Polke, Germany, b.1941: experimental and poetic artist, photographer

Francis Ponge, France, 1899-1988: poet of objects and essayist

Richard Prince, USA, b.1949: unclassifiable painter and photographer

Joseph Roth, Austria, 1894-1939: elegiac novelist, clear-eyed writer, journalist and essayist

Erika Rothenberg, USA, b.1969: artist

Willi Ruge, Germany, 1882-1961: artist, photographer

Edward Ruscha, USA, b.1937: generous painter, printmaker, filmmaker and maker of artists' books

Fritz Schwegler, Germany, b.1935: witty painter and sculptor

David Shrigley, UK, b.1968: fine artist and dark wit

Charles Simic, Yugoslavia and USA, b.1938: surrealistic poet

N. F. Simpson, UK, b.1919: absurdist playwright

John Sladek, USA, 1937-2000: 'New Wave' science fiction writer, satirist

Saul Steinberg, Romania and USA, 1914-1999: transcendentally talented draughtsman-artist

Michael Stern, Canada, contemporary writer, photographer

Piers Wardle, UK, b.1960: artist, photographer and researcher

Richard Wentworth, UK, b.1947: sculptor, teacher, animateur

Michael Woods, UK: contemporary surrealistic photographer and artist

Shi Xinning, China, b.1969: artist, photographer and wit

ACKNOWLEDGEMENTS

6: © Michael Woods, from *Paris and the Surrealists,* by George Melly and Michael Woods, Thames & Hudson, 1991
10: From *Vanishing Lung Syndrome* by Miroslav Holub, translated by David Young and Dana Hábová, Faber & Faber Ltd.,
1990 **20-21:** © Sian Bonnell **24:** © Glen Baxter **25:** © Werner Hauser. From *The Ecstasy of Things, From the
Functional Object to the Fetish in 20th Century Photographs,* Edited by Thomas Seelig and Urs Stahel, Steidl Verlag,
2005 **28:** Reproduced courtesy of the artist and Galerie Emanuel Perrotin, Paris **29:** From catalogue to exhibition
Fluxus Nella Sua Epoca, 1958-1978, Italy, 2000 **34-35:** Courtesy Fundació Joan Brossa, Barcelona **36:** © Simon
Patterson and Douglas Gordon **38-39** Courtesy Richard Wentworth and The Lisson Gallery **41:** © Jacques Carelman
42: © Piers Wardle **44:** Reproduced by permission of the Marquis of Bath, Longleat House, Warminster, Wiltshire.
Thanks to Kate Harris. **46:** From *Selected Poems* by Francis Ponge, edited by Margaret Guiton, translated by
Margaret Guiton, John Montague and C.K.Williams, Faber & Faber Ltd., 1994 **47:** Reproduced by permission of Peter
Wollen **48-49** © Sian Bonnell **51:** Richard Prince, *What A Kid I Was,* 1998, photograph Larry Lame, courtesy Barbara
Gladstone Gallery, New York **52:** © Cornelia Parker **56:** From *The Book of Disquiet* by Fernando Pessoa, translated by
Richard Zenith (Allen Lane, The Penguin Press, 2001) Copyright © Richard Zenith, 2001 **57:** Courtesy of the artist and
the Sara Melzer Gallery **58** © Les Coleman **59:** © Adam Dant **61:** From *Species of Spaces and Other Pieces* by
Georges Perec, translated by John Sturrock (Penguin, 1997). Copyright © John Sturrock, 1997 **62:** © Adam Dant **63:** ©
Michael Stern **64:** Reproduced courtesy the artist and the Lisson Gallery, London **65:** From *Franz Kafka: The
Complete Stories,* edited by Nahum N. Glatzer, copyright 1946, 1947, 1948, 1949, 1954, 1958, 1971 by Schocken Books.
Used by permission of Schocken Books, a division of Random House, Inc. *Give It Up!* translated by Tania and James
Stern, *The Departure,* translated by Tania and James Stern, *The Next Village,* translated by Willa and Edwin Muir **68:** ©
Sian Bonnell **69:** David Shrigley, *Map of the London Underground,* 2005 © London Underground commissioned by
Platform for Art, the art programme for London Underground **70:** *An Encounter* by Daniil Kharms, from *Incidences,*
Serpent's Tail, 1993 **72-73:** Courtesy the artist **75:** *The Plummeting Old Women,* by Daniil Kharms, from *Incidences,*
edited and translated by Neil Cornwell, Serpent's Tail, 1993 **78-79:** Courtesy Wim Delvoye and Gianni Degyse of the
Wim Delvoye Studio **80-81:** *Going For A Walk* by Joseph Roth, from *What I Saw; Reports from Berlin 1920-33,*
translated and introduced by Michael Hofmann, Granta Books, 2003 **83:** *Why* by Wassily Kandinsky from *Twentieth
Century Russian Poetry,* edited by Yevgeni Yevtushenko, Bantam, Doubleday, Dell. **84:** *A View of Things* by Edwin
Morgan from *Selected Poems,* Carcanet Press Ltd., 1996 **85:** © Fritz Schwegler **86:** Rejection letter published by
permission of John Kador **88-89:** *Salesmen undergoing mock initiation ceremony* © Alex Webb/Magnum Photos
92: Courtesy Wim Delvoye and Gianni Degyse of the Wim Delvoye Studio **93:** "Found" poem by Jean L'Anselme
(previously "found" by Gerard Hoffnung), translated from the French by Michael Benedikt, from *The Ring Around the
World,* Rapp & Whiting, **95:** © Sian Bonnell **99:** Courtesy the artist and the Sara Melzer Gallery **100-103:** *The Index* by
J. G. Ballard is originally from the collection *War Fever.* Now available in *The Complete Short Stories* by J. G. Ballard,
HarperCollins, London. Copyright © J. G. Ballard. All Rights reserved. Reproduced by permission of the Author c/o
Margaret Hanbury, 27 Walcot Square, London SE11 4UB **104-105:** © Brighid Lowe, photograph by David Proud **107:** ©
Anthony Earnshaw **108:** *The Information Man,* courtesy Ed Ruscha **109:** from *The Total Library; Non-Fiction 1922-
1986,* edited by Eliot Weinberger, translated by Esther Allen, Suzanne Jill Levine and Eliot Weinberger, (Allen Lane, 1991,
Penguin Books, 2001) Translation copyright © Esther Allen, Suza, 1999 **110:** From *Species of Spaces and Other Pieces*
by Georges Perec, translated by John Sturrock (Penguin, 1997) **112:** Courtesy the artist. Taken from: *herman de vries:
chance and change* by Mel Gooding, Thames and Hudson, 2006 **114-115:** Taken from *The Third Policeman* by Flann

INDEX